FOLENS MATHS WEEKLY ASSESSMENT

Book 5

Hilary Koll

Steve Mills

Folens
Publishers

Introduction

Weekly Assessment and the National Numeracy Framework

Each of the six books in this series provides 34 sharply focused assessments that address the Year's National Numeracy Framework learning objectives. They are arranged in accordance with the five divisions of each yearly teaching programme, and will help teachers to review and record the progress children are making in relation to the learning objectives during each year of school.

The assessments

Assessments consist of either written questions or a mix of written and orally delivered questions, depending on the nature of the objectives. In both cases, the format ensures quick and easy marking.

Assessment administration

Each assessment will take approximately 20–30 minutes of class time, and might follow or conclude the final Mathematics session of the week. Assessments should be selected according to what has been taught in the week. Where an assessment includes oral questions it is recommended that these are delivered at the start and that no more than 5 seconds are given for each question.

Each assessment consists of two pages – a teacher page and a pupil page.

The teacher page includes:

- a list of the learning objectives in a division of the yearly teaching programme to provide overall context, together with the specific objectives assessed in the test (highlighted in bold type) and the related question numbers

- teacher notes that point out typical misconceptions and errors and also offer teaching tips

- oral questions for those tests that include oral work

- answers.

The pupil page is a page with questions and space for answers.

In addition, there is a photocopiable record sheet provided to allow you to record weekly assessment marks for all pupils.

Acknowledgements

Folens allows photocopying of pages marked 'copiable page' for educational use, providing that this use is within the confines of the purchasing institution. Copiable pages should not be declared in any return in respect of any photocopying licence.

Folens books are protected by international copyright laws. All rights are reserved. The copyright of all materials in this book, except where otherwise stated, remains the property of the publisher and authors. No part of this publication may be reproduced, stored in a retrieval system, or transmitted, in any form or by any means, for whatever purpose, without the written permission of Folens Limited.

Hilary Koll and Steve Mills hereby assert their moral rights to be identified as the authors of this work in accordance with the Copyright, Designs and Patents Act 1988.

Editor: Hayley Willer   Layout artist: Philippa Jarvis
Cover design: Ed Gallagher   Illustrations: Susan Hutchison
Cover photograph: Kelvin Freeman (With thanks to Grove Park Primary School, Chiswick.)

© 1999 Folens Limited, on behalf of the authors.

Summary of teaching programme objectives from the *Framework for Teaching Mathematics*, published by the DfEE as part of the National Numeracy Stategy.

First published 1999 by Folens Limited, Dunstable and Dublin.

Folens Limited, Albert House, Apex Business Centre, Boscombe Road, Dunstable, LU5 4RL, United Kingdom. Reprinted 2000.

ISBN 186202 826–5

Printed in Singapore by Craft Print

Contents

Place value, ordering and rounding

Activity sheet questions

Written

1–10
- **Read and write whole numbers in figures and words, and know what each digit represents.**
- Multiply and divide any positive integer up to 10 000 by 10 or 100 and understand the effect (e.g. 9900 ÷ 10, 737 ÷ 10, 2060 ÷ 100).
- Use the vocabulary of comparing and ordering numbers, including symbols such as <, >, ≤, ≥, =.
  Give one or more numbers lying between two given numbers.
  Order a set of integers less than 1 million.
- Use the vocabulary of estimation and approximation.
  Make and justify estimates of large numbers, and estimate simple proportions such as one third, seven tenths.
  Round any integer up to 10 000 to the nearest 10, 100 or 1000.
- Order a given set of positive and negative integers (e.g. on a number line, on a temperature scale).
  Calculate a temperature rise or fall across 0°C.

Teacher note

- Emphasise that each column is worth ten times more than the column to its right. Columns to the left become larger in value and columns to the right become smaller in value. A deep understanding of this will help children in later decimal work.

Answers

1 What does the 2 represent in 34 258?

200

2 What is the value of the 5 in 65 890?

5000

3 Use digits to write this number.
Four hundred and twelve thousand, six hundred and thirty-four

412 634

4 Which is more: 8 thousands or 79 hundreds?

8 thousands

5 Write this number in words. 432 784

Four hundred and thirty-two thousand, seven hundred and eighty-four

6 Write this number in words. 701 010

Seven hundred and one thousand, and ten

7 How much needs to be added to 34 681 to change it to 37 681?

3000

8 Use digits to write this number.
Five million, thirty-seven thousand and nineteen

5 037 019

9 Add 1000 to 49 999.

50 999

10 Subtract 1000 from 34 231.

33 231

Name: _____   Date: _____

1 What does the 2 represent in 34 258?

2 What is the value of the 5 in 65 890?

3 Use digits to write this number.
Four hundred and twelve thousand, six hundred and thirty-four

4 Which is more: 8 thousands or 79 hundreds?

5 Write this number in words. 432 784

6 Write this number in words. 701,010

7 How much needs to be added to 34 681 to change it to 37 681?

8 Use digits to write this number.
Five million, thirty-seven thousand and nineteen

9 Add 1000 to 49 999.

10 Subtract 1000 from 34 231.

Activity sheet questions

Written

- Read and write whole numbers in figures and words, and know what each digit represents.

1–6
- **Multiply and divide any positive integer up to 10 000 by 10 or 100 and understand the effect (e.g. 9900 ÷ 10, 737 ÷ 10, 2060 ÷ 100).**

7–8
- **Use the vocabulary of comparing and ordering numbers, including symbols such as $<$, $>$, $\leq$, $\geq$, $=$.**

9
- **Give one or more numbers lying between two given numbers.**

10
- **Order a set of integers less than 1 million.**

- Use the vocabulary of estimation and approximation.
  Make and justify estimates of large numbers, and estimate simple proportions such as one third, seven tenths.
  Round any integer up to 10 000 to the nearest 10, 100 or 1000.

- Order a given set of positive and negative integers (e.g. on a number line, on a temperature scale).
  Calculate a temperature rise or fall across 0°C.

Teacher note

- Avoid the phrase 'add a nought', which is unhelpful when children multiply decimals by 10, e.g. 8.5 x 10 is not 8.50. Concentrate on the movement of the digits to the left or to the right when multiplying and dividing by 10, 100, etc.

Answers

1 a. What is 800 multiplied by 100? | **80 000**

b. What is 800 divided by 100? | **8**

2 a. What is 700 multiplied by 1000? | **700 000**

b. What is 700 divided by 1000? | **0.7**

3 Write one tenth of 500. | **50**

4 How many times larger than 45 is 4500? | **100**

5 How many times smaller is 234 than 2340? | **10**

6 How many of these coins are there in £500?

a. £1 | **500**   b. 10p | **5000**   c. 1p | **50 000**

7 Which is larger: 24 765 or 24 657? | **24 765**

8 True or false?

a. 60 712 > 67 012 | **False**   b. 403 901 < 409 301 | **True**

9 What number is halfway between 32 600 and 33 000? | **32 800**

10 Put these numbers in ascending order.

16 243, 16 432, 14 623, 14 326 | **14 326, 14 623, 16 243, 16 432**

Name: _____ Date: _____

1 a. What is 800 multiplied by 100? _____

  b. What is 800 divided by 100? _____

2 a. What is 700 multiplied by 1000? _____

  b. What is 700 divided by 1000? _____

3 Write one tenth of 500. _____

4 How many times larger than 45 is 4500? _____

5 How many times smaller is 234 than 2340? _____

6 How many of these coins are there in £500?

  a. £1 _____ b. 10p _____ c. 1p _____

7 Which is larger: 24 765 or 24 657? _____

8 True or false?

  a. 60 712 > 67 012 _____ b. 403 901 < 409 301 _____

9 What number is halfway between 32 600 and 33 000? _____

10 Put these numbers in ascending order.

  16 243, 16 432, 14 623, 14 326 _____

Place value, ordering and rounding

Activity sheet questions

- Read and write whole numbers in figures and words, and know what each digit represents.
- Multiply and divide any positive integer up to 10 000 by 10 or 100 and understand the effect (e.g. 9900 ÷ 10, 737 ÷ 10, 2060 ÷ 100).
- Use the vocabulary of comparing and ordering numbers, including symbols such as <, >, ≤, ≥, =.
  Give one or more numbers lying between two given numbers.
  Order a set of integers less than 1 million.

Written

1–6
- Use the vocabulary of estimation and approximation.
  Make and justify estimates of large numbers, and estimate simple proportions such as one third, seven tenths.
  Round any integer up to 10 000 to the nearest 10, 100 or 1000.

7–9
- Order a given set of positive and negative integers (e.g. on a number line, on a temperature scale).
  Calculate a temperature rise or fall across 0°C.

Teacher note

- Children's rounding skills will be improved by the use of number lines, e.g. 0_____1000, marked in hundreds. Mark a three-digit number on the line, such as 378, and it can be clearly seen which hundred it is nearest to.

Answers

1 Tick approximately how many apples, in a line, will stretch for 1 metre.

1 ☐   10 ☑   100 ☐   1000 ☐

2 Estimate how many times you breathe in, in a minute.

1 ☐   25 ☑   100 ☐   250 ☐

3 What numbers do you think are being pointed to?

0 ——↓——————↓ 1000

(Answers close to these values are acceptable.)   250   900

4 Round these numbers to the nearest 10.

a. 62 → **60**   b. 76 → **80**   c. 149 → **150**

5 Round these numbers to the nearest 100.

a. 527 → **500**   b. 851 → **900**   c. 2372 → **2400**

6 Write a number between 4000 and 5000 that is nearer to 5000.

(Any number larger than 4500, but smaller than 5000.)

7 Put these numbers in the dodgem cars in descending order.   –1, 0, –5, –3, –7

0   –1   –3   –5   –7

8 Write a number in each of the empty balloons so that they are in order.

–8   –7 / –6   –5   –4 / –3   –2   ←(Any number < –2.)

9 Put these temperatures in order, coldest first.   3°, –6°, –3°, 0°, –8°

–8°, –6°, –3°, 0°, 3°

Name: _____   Date: _____

Place value, ordering and rounding

1 Tick approximately how many apples, in a line, will stretch for 1 metre.

1 ☐   10 ☐   100 ☐   1000 ☐

2 Estimate how many times you breathe in, in a minute.

1 ☐   25 ☐   100 ☐   250 ☐

3 What numbers do you think are being pointed to?

0 ↓   ↓ 1000

☐   ☐

4 Round these numbers to the nearest 10.

a. 62 ☐   b. 76 ☐   c. 149 ☐

5 Round these numbers to the nearest 100.

a. 527 ☐   b. 851 ☐   c. 2372 ☐

6 Write a number between 4000 and 5000 that is nearer to 5000.   ☐

7 Put these numbers in the dodgem cars in descending order.   –1, 0, –5, –3, –7

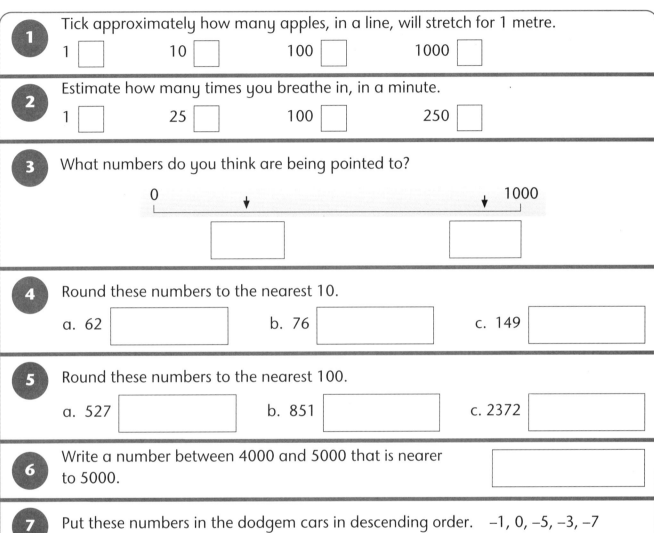

8 Write a number in each of the empty balloons so that they are in order.

–8   –5   –2

9 Put these temperatures in order, coldest first.   3°, –6°, –3°, 0°, –8°

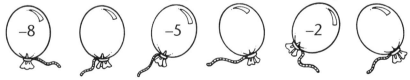

Properties of numbers and number sequences

Activity sheet questions

Oral

1–6 ● Know squares of numbers to at least 10 x 10.

7–10 ● Make general statements about odd or even numbers, including the outcome of sums and differences.

Written

1–7 ● Recognise and extend number sequences formed by counting from any number in steps of constant size, extending beyond zero when counting back. For example:
  – count on in steps of 25 to 1000, and then back;
  – count on or back in steps of 0.1, 0.2, 0.3 … .

● Recognise multiples of 6, 7, 8, 9, up to the tenth multiple. Know and apply tests of divisibility by 2, 4, 5, 10 or 100.

● Find all the pairs of factors of any number up to 100.

Teacher note

● Children need to understand that it is the units digit that determines whether a number is odd or even, however large the number.

Oral questions

1. What is 6 times 6?
2. What is 4 multiplied by 4?
3. What is the square of 5?
4. What is 7 squared?
5. What number multiplied by itself gives 81?
6. What is the area of a square where one side is 10m?
7. The sum of three odd numbers is always even. True or false?
8. The sum of three even numbers is always even. True or false?
9. The difference between an even number and an odd number is always odd. True or false?
10. The difference between two odd numbers is always odd. True or false?

Answers

1.	**36**	6.	**100m²**
2.	**16**	7.	**False**
3.	**25**	8.	**True**
4.	**49**	9.	**True**
5.	**9**	10.	**False**

1 Write the next four numbers in this sequence. 7, 14, 21 … **28, 35, 42, 49**

2 Write the next six numbers in this sequence. 300, 325, 350 …
375, 400, 425, 450, 475, 500

3 Write the next six numbers.
26 20 14 8 2 **–4 –10 –16 –22**

4 Fill in the missing numbers. 23, 32, **41**, 50, **59**

5 Fill in the missing numbers.
86 **74** 62 50 **38** 26

6 Continue the pattern on the path.
0.6 0.7 0.8 **0.9** **1.0** **1.1** **1.2** **1.3**

7 Fill in the bricks.
2.2 2.1 **2.0** **1.9** 1.8 **1.7**

Name: _____   Date: _____

1.	6.
2.	7.
3.	8.
4.	9.
5.	10.

1 Write the next four numbers in this sequence.   7, 14, 21 …   [   ]

2 Write the next six numbers in this sequence.   300, 325, 350 …

[   ]

3 Write the next six numbers.

26   20   14

4 Fill in the missing numbers.   23, 32, [   ] , 50, [   ]

5 Fill in the missing numbers.

86   74   38

6 Continue the pattern on the path.

0.6   0.7   0.8

7 Fill in the bricks.   2.2   2.1   [   ]   [   ]   1.8

Properties of numbers and number sequences

Activity sheet questions

- Recognise and extend number sequences formed by counting from any number in steps of constant size, extending beyond zero when counting back. For example:
  - count on in steps of 25 to 1000, and then back;
  - count on or back in steps of 0.1, 0.2, 0.3 ... .
- Make general statements about odd or even numbers, including the outcome of sums and differences.
- Know squares of numbers to at least 10 x 10.

Written

1–6
- **Recognise multiples of 6, 7, 8, 9, up to the tenth multiple.**
  Know and apply tests of divisibility by 2, 4, 5, 10 or 100.

7–10
- **Find all the pairs of factors of any number up to 100.**

Teacher note

- A sound knowledge of tests of divisibility is invaluable when needing to find all the factors of a number.
- A factor is a whole number that when multiplied with another whole number produces a given number.

Answers

1 Draw circles around the numbers that are exactly divisible by 6.

14   (24)   (42)   56   64   46

2 Write five numbers that are exactly divisible by 7. | **(Any five numbers divisible by 7.)**

3 Draw circles around the numbers that are divisible by 8.

36   18   42   (56)   (64)   (72)

4 Write a number in each box that can be divided by 9, with no remainder.

| | | **(Any six numbers divisible by 9.)** | | |

5 Draw circles around the numbers that divide into 42, with no remainder.

(1) (2) (3) 4 5 (6) (7) 8 9 10

6 Draw circles around the numbers that divide into 72, with no remainder.

(1) (2) (3) (4) 5 (6) 7 (8) (9) 10

7 Write on the washing line the factors of the number in the basket.

30 | 1 30 2 15 3 10 5 6

8 How many factors does the number 36 have? | **9**

9 Write the pairs of factors for the number 40. | **1, 40; 2, 20; 4, 10; 5, 8**

10 Write the pairs of factors for the number 48. | **1, 48; 2, 24; 3, 16; 4, 12; 6, 8**

Name: _____ Date: _____

Properties of numbers and number sequences

1 Draw circles around the numbers that are exactly divisible by 6.

14   24   42   56   64   46

2 Write five numbers that are exactly divisible by 7. [   ]

3 Draw circles around the numbers that are divisible by 8.

36   18   42   56   64   72

4 Write a number in each box that can be divided by 9, with no remainder.

[   ]   [   ]   [   ]   [   ]   [   ]   [   ]

5 Draw circles around the numbers that divide into 42, with no remainder.

1   2   3   4   5   6   7   8   9   10

6 Draw circles around the numbers that divide into 72, with no remainder.

1   2   3   4   5   6   7   8   9   10

7 Write on the washing line the factors of the number in the basket.

8 How many factors does the number 36 have? [   ]

9 Write the pairs of factors for the number 40. [   ]

10 Write the pairs of factors for the number 48. [   ]

Activity sheet questions

Written

1–10
- Use fraction notation, including mixed numbers, and the vocabulary 'numerator' and 'denominator'.
  Change an improper fraction to a mixed number (e.g. change $\frac{13}{10}$ to $1\frac{3}{10}$).
  Recognise when two simple fractions are equivalent, including relating hundredths to tenths (e.g. $\frac{70}{100} = \frac{7}{10}$).
- Order a set of fractions such as 2, $2\frac{3}{4}$, $1\frac{3}{4}$, $2\frac{1}{2}$, $1\frac{1}{2}$, and position them on a number line.
- Relate fractions to division, and use division to find simple fractions, including tenths and hundredths, of numbers and quantities (e.g. $\frac{3}{4}$ of 12, $\frac{1}{10}$ of 50, $\frac{1}{100}$ of £3).
- Solve simple problems using ideas of ratio and proportion ('one for every …' and 'one in every …').

Teacher note

- Avoid only showing sequences that are formed in the same way, e.g. by doubling. Children can form the misconception that fractions are only equivalent if they can be doubled, thus thinking that $\frac{1}{4}$ and $\frac{3}{12}$ are not equivalent.

Answers

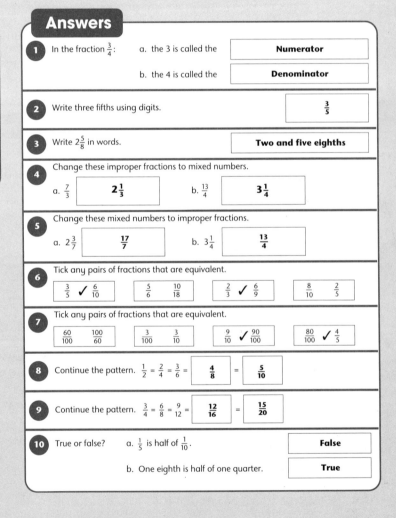

1 In the fraction $\frac{3}{4}$:   a. the 3 is called the **Numerator**

     b. the 4 is called the **Denominator**

2 Write three fifths using digits. $\frac{3}{5}$

3 Write $2\frac{5}{8}$ in words.   **Two and five eighths**

4 Change these improper fractions to mixed numbers.

   a. $\frac{7}{3}$ **$2\frac{1}{3}$**   b. $\frac{13}{4}$ **$3\frac{1}{4}$**

5 Change these mixed numbers to improper fractions.

   a. $2\frac{3}{7}$ **$\frac{17}{7}$**   b. $3\frac{1}{4}$ **$\frac{13}{4}$**

6 Tick any pairs of fractions that are equivalent.

   $\frac{3}{5}$ ✓ $\frac{6}{10}$ $\frac{5}{6}$ $\frac{10}{18}$ $\frac{2}{3}$ ✓ $\frac{6}{9}$ $\frac{8}{10}$ $\frac{2}{5}$

7 Tick any pairs of fractions that are equivalent.

   $\frac{60}{100}$ $\frac{100}{60}$ $\frac{3}{100}$ $\frac{3}{10}$ $\frac{9}{10}$ ✓ $\frac{90}{100}$ $\frac{80}{100}$ ✓ $\frac{4}{5}$

8 Continue the pattern. $\frac{1}{2} = \frac{2}{4} = \frac{3}{6} =$ **$\frac{4}{8}$** $=$ **$\frac{5}{10}$**

9 Continue the pattern. $\frac{3}{4} = \frac{6}{8} = \frac{9}{12} =$ **$\frac{12}{16}$** $=$ **$\frac{15}{20}$**

10 True or false?   a. $\frac{1}{5}$ is half of $\frac{1}{10}$.   **False**

     b. One eighth is half of one quarter.   **True**

Name: _____ Date: _____

Fractions, decimals, percentages, ratio and proportion

1 In the fraction $\frac{3}{4}$: a. the 3 is called the [   ]

b. the 4 is called the [   ]

2 Write three fifths using digits. [   ]

3 Write $2\frac{5}{8}$ in words. [   ]

4 Change these improper fractions to mixed numbers.

a. $\frac{7}{3}$ [   ]   b. $\frac{13}{4}$ [   ]

5 Change these mixed numbers to improper fractions.

a. $2\frac{3}{7}$ [   ]   b. $3\frac{1}{4}$ [   ]

6 Tick any pairs of fractions that are equivalent.

| $\frac{3}{5}$ $\frac{6}{10}$ | $\frac{5}{6}$ $\frac{10}{18}$ | $\frac{2}{3}$ $\frac{6}{9}$ | $\frac{8}{10}$ $\frac{2}{5}$ |

7 Tick any pairs of fractions that are equivalent.

| $\frac{60}{100}$ $\frac{100}{60}$ | $\frac{3}{100}$ $\frac{3}{10}$ | $\frac{9}{10}$ $\frac{90}{100}$ | $\frac{80}{100}$ $\frac{4}{5}$ |

8 Continue the pattern. $\frac{1}{2} = \frac{2}{4} = \frac{3}{6} =$ [   ] $=$ [   ]

9 Continue the pattern. $\frac{3}{4} = \frac{6}{8} = \frac{9}{12} =$ [   ] $=$ [   ]

10 True or false? a. $\frac{1}{5}$ is half of $\frac{1}{10}$. [   ]

b. One eighth is half of one quarter. [   ]

Activity sheet questions

Oral
1–10

Written
1–3

4–5

- Use fraction notation, including mixed numbers, and the vocabulary 'numerator' and 'denominator'.
  Change an improper fraction to a mixed number (e.g. change $\frac{13}{10}$ to $1\frac{3}{10}$).
  Recognise when two simple fractions are equivalent, including relating hundredths to tenths (e.g. $\frac{70}{100} = \frac{7}{10}$).

- Relate fractions to division, and use division to find simple fractions, including tenths and hundredths, of numbers and quantities (e.g. $\frac{3}{4}$ of 12, $\frac{1}{10}$ of 50, $\frac{1}{100}$ of £3).

- Order a set of fractions such as 2, $2\frac{3}{4}$, $1\frac{3}{4}$, $2\frac{1}{2}$, $1\frac{1}{2}$, and position them on a number line.

- Solve simple problems using ideas of ratio and proportion ('one for every …' and 'one in every …').

Teacher note

- Stress the multiplication aspect of ratio, as in twice as many or three times as many. Addition strategies, as in add 1 for every blue sweet, should be avoided.

Oral questions

1. What is one tenth of 80?
2. What is one third of 90?
3. Find one sixth of 24.
4. What is $\frac{3}{10}$ of 50?
5. What is $\frac{3}{4}$ of 40?
6. Find $\frac{3}{10}$ of 1m in cm.
7. What fraction of £1 is 25p?
8. What fraction of 1m is 91cm?
9. What fraction of 1 day is 6 hours?
10. What fraction of 1kg is 750g?

Answers

1. **8**	6. **30cm**
2. **30**	7. $\frac{1}{4}$
3. **4**	8. $\frac{91}{100}$
4. **15**	9. $\frac{1}{4}$
5. **30**	10. $\frac{3}{4}$

1 Hang these fractions on the washing line in order of size, smallest first.

$\frac{1}{2}$, $2\frac{1}{2}$, $2\frac{1}{4}$, $\frac{3}{4}$, $1\frac{3}{4}$ $\frac{1}{2}$ $\frac{3}{4}$ $1\frac{3}{4}$ $2\frac{1}{4}$ $2\frac{1}{2}$

2 Mark these fractions on the number line. $\frac{7}{10}$, $\frac{3}{10}$, $\frac{1}{2}$, $\frac{1}{10}$, $\frac{4}{5}$, $\frac{1}{5}$

0   $\frac{1}{10}$ $\frac{1}{5}$ $\frac{3}{10}$ $\frac{1}{2}$ $\frac{7}{10}$ $\frac{4}{5}$ 1

3 Write the fractions being pointed to.

$\frac{2}{10}$ or $\frac{1}{5}$ $\frac{6}{10}$ or $\frac{3}{5}$ $\frac{9}{10}$

0 ↓ ↓ ↓ 1

4 A packet of sweets contains 3 red sweets for every 1 blue sweet.
  a. How many blue sweets are there if there are 24 red sweets? **8**
  b. How many red sweets are there if there are 11 blue sweets? **33**

5 A music shop has 5 CDs for every 2 tapes.
  a. How many tapes are there if the shop has 100 CDs? **40**
  b. How many CDs are there if the shop has 60 tapes? **150**

Name: _____ Date: _____

1.	6.
2.	7.
3.	8.
4.	9.
5.	10.

1 Hang these fractions on the washing line in order of size, smallest first.

$\frac{1}{2}$, $2\frac{1}{2}$, $2\frac{1}{4}$, $\frac{3}{4}$, $1\frac{3}{4}$

2 Mark these fractions on the number line. $\frac{7}{10}$, $\frac{3}{10}$, $\frac{1}{2}$, $\frac{1}{10}$, $\frac{4}{5}$, $\frac{1}{5}$

0 ———————————————————————— 1

3 Write the fractions being pointed to.

0 ———————————————————————— 1

4 A packet of sweets contains 3 red sweets for every 1 blue sweet.

a. How many blue sweets are there if there are 24 red sweets?

b. How many red sweets are there if there are 11 blue sweets?

5 A music shop has 5 CDs for every 2 tapes.

a. How many tapes are there if the shop has 100 CDs?

b. How many CDs are there if the shop has 60 tapes?

Activity sheet questions

Written

1–6 ● Use decimal notation for tenths and hundredths.
Know what each digit represents in a number with up to two decimal places.

7–9 Order a set of numbers or measurements with the same number of decimal places.

● Round a number with one or two decimal places to the nearest integer.

● Relate fractions to their decimal representations: that is, recognise the equivalence between the decimal and fraction forms of one half, one quarter, three quarters … and tenths and hundredths (e.g. $\frac{7}{10} = 0.7$, $\frac{27}{100} = 0.27$).

● Begin to understand percentage as the number of parts in every 100, and find simple percentages of small whole-number quantities (e.g. 25% of £8). Express one half, one quarter, three quarters, and tenths and hundredths, as percentages (e.g. know that $\frac{3}{4} = 75\%$).

Teacher note

● Children often use a 'longer is larger' strategy when ordering decimals, thus giving 0.75 as larger than 0.8. Further work on the value of the columns after the decimal point may be necessary.

Answers

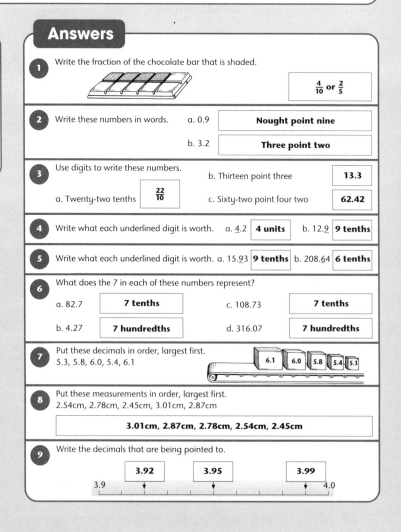

1 Write the fraction of the chocolate bar that is shaded.

$\frac{4}{10}$ or $\frac{2}{5}$

2 Write these numbers in words.

a. 0.9 — **Nought point nine**

b. 3.2 — **Three point two**

3 Use digits to write these numbers.

a. Twenty-two tenths — $\frac{22}{10}$

b. Thirteen point three — **13.3**

c. Sixty-two point four two — **62.42**

4 Write what each underlined digit is worth. a. 4.2 **4 units** b. 12.9 **9 tenths**

5 Write what each underlined digit is worth. a. 15.93 **9 tenths** b. 208.64 **6 tenths**

6 What does the 7 in each of these numbers represent?

a. 82.7 **7 tenths**

c. 108.73 **7 tenths**

b. 4.27 **7 hundredths**

d. 316.07 **7 hundredths**

7 Put these decimals in order, largest first.
5.3, 5.8, 6.0, 5.4, 6.1

6.1 6.0 5.8 5.4 5.3

8 Put these measurements in order, largest first.
2.54cm, 2.78cm, 2.45cm, 3.01cm, 2.87cm

3.01cm, 2.87cm, 2.78cm, 2.54cm, 2.45cm

9 Write the decimals that are being pointed to.

3.92   **3.95**   **3.99**

3.9 |————————————| 4.0

8 Fractions, decimals, percentages, ratio and proportion

1 Write the fraction of the chocolate bar that is shaded.

2 Write these numbers in words.   a. 0.9

b. 3.2

3 Use digits to write these numbers.

b. Thirteen point three

a. Twenty-two tenths

c. Sixty-two point four two

4 Write what each underlined digit is worth.   a. 4.2   b. 12.9

5 Write what each underlined digit is worth. a. 15.93   b. 208.64

6 What does the 7 in each of these numbers represent?

a. 82.7

c. 108.73

b. 4.27

d. 316.07

7 Put these decimals in order, largest first.
5.3, 5.8, 6.0, 5.4, 6.1

8 Put these measurements in order, largest first.
2.54cm, 2.78cm, 2.45cm, 3.01cm, 2.87cm

9 Write the decimals that are being pointed to.

3.9   4.0

Activity sheet questions

- Use decimal notation for tenths and hundredths.
  Know what each digit represents in a number with up to two decimal places.
  Order a set of numbers or measurements with the same number of decimal places.

Oral
1–10
Written
1–6

- **Round a number with one or two decimal places to the nearest integer.**

- **Relate fractions to their decimal representations: that is, recognise the equivalence between the decimal and fraction forms of one half, one quarter, three quarters … and tenths and hundredths (e.g. $\frac{7}{10}$ = 0.7, $\frac{27}{100}$ = 0.27).**

- Begin to understand percentage as the number of parts in every 100, and find simple percentages of small whole-number quantities (e.g. 25% of £8).
  Express one half, one quarter, three quarters, and tenths and hundredths, as percentages (e.g. know that $\frac{3}{4}$ = 75%).

Teacher note

- Children need to understand that zero is an integer and that rounded numbers can equal zero, e.g. 0.2 rounded to the nearest integer equals zero.

Oral questions

Round these decimals to the nearest whole number.

1. 12.7
2. 18.6
3. 27.1
4. 34.3
5. 54.5

Round these prices to the nearest pound.

6. £3.45
7. £6.71
8. £12.49
9. £9.52
10. £23.50

Answers

1. **13**	6. **£3**
2. **19**	7. **£7**
3. **27**	8. **£12**
4. **34**	9. **£10**
5. **55**	10. **£24**

1 Write the equivalent fraction for each of these decimals.

a. 0.5 $\frac{1}{2}$ b. 0.25 $\frac{1}{4}$ c. 0.75 $\frac{3}{4}$ d. 0.1 $\frac{1}{10}$

2 Write the equivalent decimal for each of these fractions.

a. $\frac{6}{10}$ **0.6**   b. $\frac{9}{10}$ **0.9**   c. $\frac{50}{100}$ **0.5**   d. $\frac{1}{100}$ **0.01**

3 Tick the decimal that is equal to $\frac{93}{100}$.

9.3 ☐   93.0 ☐   0.93 ✓   9.03 ☐

4 Tick the fraction that is equal to 8.51.

$\frac{85}{1}$ ☐ $8\frac{51}{10}$ ☐ $8\frac{5}{1}$ ☐ $\frac{851}{100}$ ✓

5 Write these measurements as decimals.   a. $6\frac{3}{10}$ kg   **6.3kg**   b. $9\frac{47}{100}$ m   **9.47m**

6 Write these measurements as fractions.   a. 57.3 l   **$57\frac{3}{10}$ l**   b. 12.39cm   **$12\frac{39}{100}$ cm**

Name: _____ Date: _____

 ASSESSMENT 9 Fractions, decimals, percentages, ratio and proportion

1.	6.
2.	7.
3.	8.
4.	9.
5.	10.

1 Write the equivalent fraction for each of these decimals.

a. 0.5 [ ]   b. 0.25 [ ]   c. 0.75 [ ]   d. 0.1 [ ]

2 Write the equivalent decimal for each of these fractions.

a. $\frac{6}{10}$ [ ]   b. $\frac{9}{10}$ [ ]   c. $\frac{50}{100}$ [ ]   d. $\frac{1}{100}$ [ ]

3 Tick the decimal that is equal to $\frac{93}{100}$.

9.3 [ ]   93.0 [ ]   0.93 [ ]   9.03 [ ]

4 Tick the fraction that is equal to 8.51.

$\frac{85}{1}$ [ ] $8\frac{51}{10}$ [ ] $8\frac{5}{1}$ [ ] $\frac{851}{100}$ [ ]

5 Write these measurements as decimals. a. $6\frac{3}{10}$ kg [ ]   b. $9\frac{47}{100}$ m [ ]

6 Write these measurements as fractions. a. 57.3 l [ ]   b. 12.39cm [ ]

10 Fractions, decimals, percentages, ratio and proportion

Activity sheet questions

- Use decimal notation for tenths and hundredths.
  Know what each digit represents in a number with up to two decimal places.
  Order a set of numbers or measurements with the same number of decimal places.
- Round a number with one or two decimal places to the nearest integer.
- Relate fractions to their decimal representations: that is, recognise the equivalence between the decimal and fraction forms of one half, one quarter, three quarters … and tenths and hundredths (e.g. $\frac{7}{10} = 0.7$, $\frac{27}{100} = 0.27$).

Written

1–3 • **Begin to understand percentage as the number of parts in every 100.**

4–7 **Find simple percentages of small whole-number quantities (e.g. 25% of £8).**

8 **Express one half, one quarter, three quarters, and tenths and hundredths, as percentages (e.g. know that $\frac{3}{4}$ = 75%).**

Teacher note

- Finding 10% of a number can form the basis of other quantities, e.g. if we know that 10% is 5, then we double 5 to find 20% and multiply by 6 to find 60%.

Answers

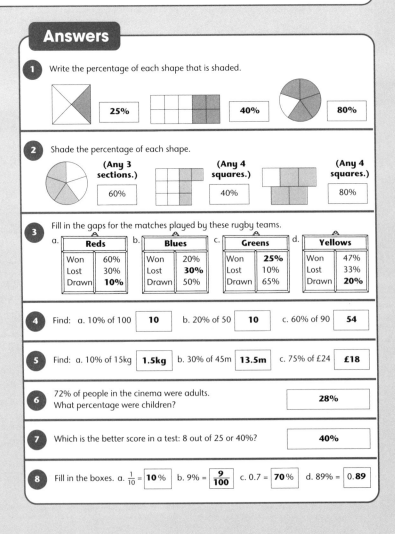

1 Write the percentage of each shape that is shaded.

25%   40%   80%

2 Shade the percentage of each shape.

(Any 3 sections.) 60%   (Any 4 squares.) 40%   (Any 4 squares.) 80%

3 Fill in the gaps for the matches played by these rugby teams.

a. **Reds** — Won 60%, Lost 30%, Drawn **10%**

b. **Blues** — Won 20%, Lost **30%**, Drawn 50%

c. **Greens** — Won **25%**, Lost 10%, Drawn 65%

d. **Yellows** — Won 47%, Lost 33%, Drawn **20%**

4 Find: a. 10% of 100 **10**   b. 20% of 50 **10**   c. 60% of 90 **54**

5 Find: a. 10% of 15kg **1.5kg**   b. 30% of 45m **13.5m**   c. 75% of £24 **£18**

6 72% of people in the cinema were adults. What percentage were children?   **28%**

7 Which is the better score in a test: 8 out of 25 or 40%?   **40%**

8 Fill in the boxes. a. $\frac{1}{10}$ = **10**%   b. 9% = $\frac{\boxed{9}}{100}$ c. 0.7 = **70**%   d. 89% = **0.89**

10 Fractions, decimals, percentages, ratio and proportion

1 Write the percentage of each shape that is shaded.

2 Shade the percentage of each shape.

 60%   40%    80%

3 Fill in the gaps for the matches played by these rugby teams.

a.
Reds	
Won	60%
Lost	30%
Drawn	

b.
Blues	
Won	20%
Lost	
Drawn	50%

c.
Greens	
Won	
Lost	10%
Drawn	65%

d.
Yellows	
Won	47%
Lost	33%
Drawn	

4 Find: a. 10% of 100 [ ]   b. 20% of 50 [ ]   c. 60% of 90 [ ]

5 Find: a. 10% of 15kg [ ]   b. 30% of 45m [ ]   c. 75% of £24 [ ]

6 72% of people in the cinema were adults.
What percentage were children? [ ]

7 Which is the better score in a test: 8 out of 25 or 40%? [ ]

8 Fill in the boxes. a. $\frac{1}{10}$ = [ ] %   b. 9% = [ ]────   c. 0.7 = [ ] %   d. 89% = 0.[ ]

Activity sheet questions

Written

1–3
- Find differences by counting up through the next multiple of 10, 100 or 1000, e.g. calculate mentally a difference such as 8006 – 2993.

4–5
- Partition into H, T and U, adding the most significant digits first.

6–8
- Identify near doubles, such as 1.5 + 1.6.
- Add or subtract the nearest multiple of 10 or 100, then adjust.
- Develop further the relationship between addition and subtraction.
- Add several numbers (e.g. four or five single digits, or multiples of 10 such as 40 + 50 + 80).
- Use known number facts and place value for mental addition and subtraction (e.g. 470 + 380, 810 – 380, 7.4 + 9.8, 9.2 – 8.6).

Teacher note

- When adding or subtracting pairs of decimals, children can make errors by treating the final tenth as a whole number, e.g. 3.5 + 3.6 = (3.5 x 2) + 1 = 8. Further work on the value of 0.1 may be necessary.

Answers

1 a. 83 – 59 = **24**   b. 107 – 86 = **21**

2 a. 304 – 192 = **112**   b. 804 – 375 = **429**

3 a. 6000 – 3992 = **2008**   b. 7000 – 5991 = **1009**

4 56 can be written as 50 + 6. Split up the following numbers in the same way.

a. 351 = **300 + 50 + 1**   c. 768 = **700 + 60 + 8**

b. 860 = **800 + 60**   d. 901 = **900 + 1**

5 Do the following sums by splitting up like this. 65 + 43 = (60 + 40) + (5 + 3) = 108

a. 74 + 58 = **(70 + 50) + (4 + 8) = 132**

b. 476 + 39 = **(400 + 0) + (70 + 30) + (6 + 9) = 515**

c. 584 – 63 = **(500 – 0) + (80 – 60) + (4 – 3) = 521**

6 240 people visited the school fair on Saturday and 230 came on Sunday. How many people visited the fair? **470**

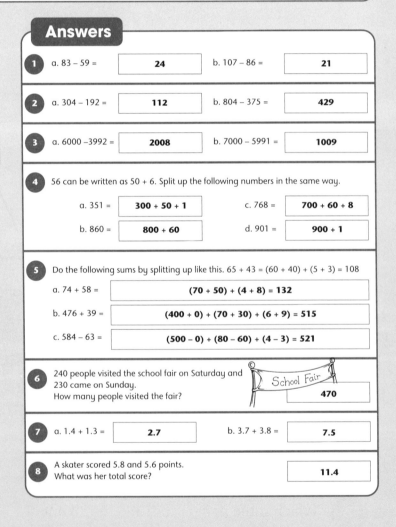

7 a. 1.4 + 1.3 = **2.7**   b. 3.7 + 3.8 = **7.5**

8 A skater scored 5.8 and 5.6 points. What was her total score? **11.4**

Mental calculation strategies (+ and –)

1 a. 83 – 59 = [ ]   b. 107 – 86 = [ ]

2 a. 304 – 192 = [ ]   b. 804 – 375 = [ ]

3 a. 6000 – 3992 = [ ]   b. 7000 – 5991 = [ ]

4 56 can be written as 50 + 6. Split up the following numbers in the same way.

   a. 351 = [ ]   c. 768 = [ ]

   b. 860 = [ ]   d. 901 = [ ]

5 Do the following sums by splitting up like this. 65 + 43 = (60 + 40) + (5 + 3) = 108

   a. 74 + 58 = [ ]

   b. 476 + 39 = [ ]

   c. 584 – 63 = [ ]

6 240 people visited the school fair on Saturday and 230 came on Sunday.
How many people visited the fair? [ ]

7 a. 1.4 + 1.3 = [ ]   b. 3.7 + 3.8 = [ ]

8 A skater scored 5.8 and 5.6 points.
What was her total score? [ ]

ASSESSMENT 12 — Mental calculation strategies (+ and –)

Activity sheet questions

- Find differences by counting up through next multiple of 10, 100 or 1000, e.g. calculate mentally a difference such as 8006 – 2993.
- Partition into H, T and U, adding the most significant digits first.
- Identify near doubles, such as 1.5 + 1.6.

Oral 1–10
- Use known number facts and place value for mental addition and subtraction (e.g. 470 + 380, 810 – 380, 7.4 + 9.8, 9.2 – 8.6).

Written
1–3
- Add several numbers (e.g. four or five single digits, or multiples of 10 such as 40 + 50 + 80).

4–5
- Develop further the relationship between addition and subtraction.

6
- Add or subtract the nearest multiple of 10 or 100, then adjust.

Teacher note

- Discuss other strategies, e.g. when adding 11, add 10 and add a further 1, etc. Remind children that the order does not matter when adding.

Oral questions

1. 270 plus 330.
2. What is the sum of 528 and 300?
3. 460 add 570 equals what?
4. 541 minus 50.
5. What is the difference between 782 and 90?
6. 651 subtract 310.
7. 1241 minus 500.
8. 341 plus what equals 500?
9. 6.5 add 8.7.
10. 3.4 plus what equals 4?

Answers

1.	**600**	6.	**341**
2.	**828**	7.	**741**
3.	**1030**	8.	**159**
4.	**491**	9.	**15.2**
5.	**692**	10.	**0.6**

1 Add these numbers.

a. 3 + 4 + 7 + 8 = **22**   c. 6 + 7 + 5 + 8 = **26**

b. 5 + 7 + 3 + 8 + 2 = **25**   d. 8 + 9 + 7 + 1 + 2 = **27**

2 Find the sum of these numbers.

a. 60 + 90 + 40 = **190**

b. 70 + 50 + 30 = **150**

3 Write the total of these numbers.

a. 14 + 26 + 15 = **55**

b. 29 + 33 + 21 = **83**

4
a. 65 + 11 = **76**

b. 132 – 11 = **121**

c. 245 – 9 = **236**

5
a. 136 + 21 = **157**

b. 347 – 29 = **318**

c. 412 – 59 = **353**

6 Use the + and – signs to write as many number sentences as you can with these numbers. 156, 234, 390

156 + 234 = 390, 390 – 156 = 234, 390 – 234 = 156

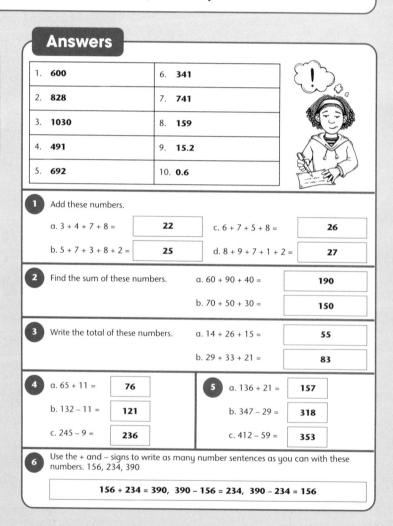

Name: _____   Date: _____

Mental calculation strategies (+ and -)

1.	6.
2.	7.
3.	8.
4.	9.
5.	10.

1 Add these numbers.

a. 3 + 4 + 7 + 8 = [ ]   c. 6 + 7 + 5 + 8 = [ ]

b. 5 + 7 + 3 + 8 + 2 = [ ]   d. 8 + 9 + 7 + 1 + 2 = [ ]

2 Find the sum of these numbers.

a. 60 + 90 + 40 = [ ]

b. 70 + 50 + 30 = [ ]

3 Write the total of these numbers.

a. 14 + 26 + 15 = [ ]

b. 29 + 33 + 21 = [ ]

4
a. 65 + 11 = [ ]

b. 132 – 11 = [ ]

c. 245 – 9 = [ ]

5
a. 136 + 21 = [ ]

b. 347 – 29 = [ ]

c. 412 – 59 = [ ]

6 Use the + and – signs to write as many number sentences as you can with these numbers. 156, 234, 390

[ ]

Pencil and paper procedures (+ and −)

Activity sheet questions

Written	• Extend written methods to:
1–2	– column addition of two integers less than 10 000
3–4	– column subtraction of two integers less than 10 000
5	– addition of more than two integers less than 10 000
6–7	– addition or subtraction of a pair of decimal fractions, both with one decimal place or both with two decimal places (e.g. £29.78 + £53.34).

Teacher note

• Check that the children can do calculations when the numbers are written horizontally, e.g. 53 + 79, before beginning this sheet as the calculations here involve the extra step of putting the numbers into the correct columns.

Answers

1

a.
```
  254
+345
-----
  599
```

b.
```
  762
+246
-----
 1008
```

c.
```
 2737
+ 255
-----
 2992
```

2 Nita scored 4827 points on her first try at a pinball game. On her second try she scored 2594 points. What was her total score?   **7421**

3 4532 supporters were at a football match. 3251 left early. How many stayed until the end?   **1281**

4

a.
```
 2783
−1496
-----
 1287
```

b.
```
 4762
−3874
-----
  888
```

c.
```
 4800
−3287
-----
 1513
```

d.
```
 7000
−4369
-----
 2631
```

5

a.
```
  345
  469
+271
-----
 1085
```

b.
```
 4572
 2838
+1905
-----
 9315
```

6

a.
```
  6.4
+1.5
-----
  7.9
```

b.
```
  8.2
+3.7
-----
 11.9
```

c.
```
 14.72 kg
+ 3.99 kg
--------
 18.71 kg
```

7

a.
```
  9.5 kg
−6.3 kg
-------
  3.2 kg
```

b.
```
 24.0 mm
−17.6 mm
--------
  6.4 mm
```

c.
```
 23.04
−17.58
------
  5.46
```

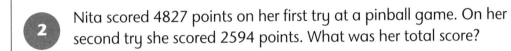

Pencil and paper procedures (+ and −)

1
a.
```
  254
+ 345
------
```

b.
```
  762
+ 246
------
```

c.
```
 2737
+  255
------
```

2 Nita scored 4827 points on her first try at a pinball game. On her second try she scored 2594 points. What was her total score?

3 4532 supporters were at a football match.
3251 left early. How many stayed until the end?

4
a.
```
 2783
-1496
------
```

b.
```
 4762
-3874
------
```

c.
```
 4800
-3287
------
```

d.
```
 7000
-4369
------
```

5
a.
```
  345
  469
+ 271
------
```

b.
```
 4572
 2838
+1905
------
```

6
a.
```
  6.4
+ 1.5
------
```

b.
```
  8.2
+ 3.7
------
```

c.
```
 14.72 kg
+ 3.99 kg
---------
```

7
a.
```
  9.5 kg
- 6.3 kg
--------
```

b.
```
 24.0 mm
-17.6 mm
--------
```

c.
```
 23.04
-17.58
------
```

Understanding multiplication and division

Activity sheet questions

Written

1-9
- Understand the effect of and relationships between the four operations, and the principles (not the names) of the arithmetic laws as they apply to multiplication.
  Begin to use brackets.
- Begin to express a quotient as a fraction, or as a decimal when dividing a whole number by 2, 4, 5 or 10, or when dividing £.p.
  Round up or down after division, depending on the context.

Teacher note

- Note the arithmetic laws as they apply to multiplication:
  1. **commutative**, i.e. 5 x 3 and 3 x 5 give the same answer
  2. **associative**, i.e. the grouping of numbers to be multiplied does not matter, e.g. (6 x 4) x 3 = 6 x (4 x 3)
  3. **distributive**, i.e. numbers to be multiplied can be split into parts and each multiplied separately, e.g. 15 x 6 = (10 x 6) + (5 x 6).

Answers

1 79 x 9 = 711
Using the same numbers, what other multiplication question equals 711?

> **9 x 79**

2 9 x 2 x 15
Use brackets to show an easier way of working this out.

> **9 x (2 x 15)**

3 8 x 32
Write an easier way of working this out.

> **(8 x 30) + (8 x 2)**

4 7 x 9 = 63   What other number sentences can you write with these numbers?

> **9 x 7 = 63, 63 ÷ 7 = 9, 63 ÷ 9 = 7**

5 True or false?

a. 63 x 0 = 63

> **False**

b. 473 x 0 = 0

> **True**

6 True or false?

a. 81 ÷ 9 = 9 ÷ 81

> **False**

b. 132 ÷ 11 = 11 ÷ 132

> **False**

7 What other number sentences can you write with these numbers? 108 ÷ 12 = 9

> **108 ÷ 9 = 12, 9 x 12 = 108, 12 x 9 = 108**

8 What calculation could you do to check whether this is correct? 252 ÷ 12 = 21

> **12 x 21 = 252**

9 a. 4 + (6 x 3) = **22**   b. 5 + (15 ÷ 5) = **8**

Name: _____ Date: _____

Understanding multiplication and division

1 79 x 9 = 711
Using the same numbers, what other multiplication question
equals 711? [   ]

2 9 x 2 x 15
Use brackets to show an easier way of working this out. [   ]

3 8 x 32
Write an easier way of working this out. [   ]

4 7 x 9 = 63   What other number sentences can you write with these numbers?

[   ]

5 True or false?

a. 63 x 0 = 63

[   ]

b. 473 x 0 = 0

[   ]

6 True or false?

a. 81 ÷ 9 = 9 ÷ 81

[   ]

b. 132 ÷ 11 = 11 ÷ 132

[   ]

7 What other number sentences can you write with these numbers? 108 ÷12 = 9

[   ]

8 What calculation could you do to check whether this is correct? 252 ÷ 12 = 21

[   ]

9 a. 4 + (6 x 3) = [   ]   b. 5 + (15 ÷ 5) = [   ]

MATHS WEEKLY ASSESSMENT: *Book 5*

Activity sheet questions

Oral

1-10 ● Understand the effect of and relationships between the four operations, and the principles (not the names) of the arithmetic laws as they apply to multiplication.
Begin to use brackets.

Written

1-2 ● Begin to express a quotient as a fraction, or as a decimal when dividing a whole number by 2, 4, 5 or 10, or when dividing £.p.

3-5 Round up or down after division, depending on the context.

Teacher note

● It is important to give division questions that are not difficult to draw the children's attention to rounding numbers up or down.
● The quotient is the answer obtained by dividing one number by another.

Oral questions

1. 6 multiplied by 9.
2. What is the product of 8 and 7?
3. Multiply 6 by 7 by 0.
4. 5 multiplied by what equals 4.5?
5. 4 multiplied by what equals 0.24?
6. Divide 36 by 4.
7. Share 72 sweets between 9 people.
8. How many boxes of 6 eggs are there in a crate labelled 54 eggs?
9. What is the remainder when 62 is divided by 6?
10. What is the quotient when 6 bags of 8 sweets are shared between 4 people?

Answers

1. **54**	6. **9**
2. **56**	7. **8**
3. **0**	8. **9**
4. **0.9**	9. **2**
5. **0.06**	10. **12**

1 Answer these questions, writing any remainder as a fraction.

a. $44 \div 8 = $ | $5\frac{1}{2}$

b. $63 \div 10 = $ | $6\frac{3}{10}$

2 Answer these questions, writing any remainder as a decimal.

a. $77 \div 10 = $ | **7.7**

c. $41 \div 2 = $ | **20.5**

b. $33 \div 4 = $ | **8.25**

d. $64 \div 5 = $ | **12.8**

3 Tanya has £140. She wants to buy some cassette tapes at £12 each. How many can she buy? | **11**

4 Mrs Murphy is building shelves for her books. Each shelf holds 36 books and she has 150 books. How many shelves will she need? | **5**

5 180 people have booked seats on a coach to go to the beach. Each coach holds 46 people. How many coaches will be needed? | **4**

ASSESSMENT 15 ## Understanding multiplication and division

1.	6.
2.	7.
3.	8.
4.	9.
5.	10.

1 Answer these questions, writing any remainder as a fraction.

a. $44 \div 8 = $ [ ]   b. $63 \div 10 = $ [ ]

2 Answer these questions, writing any remainder as a decimal.

a. $77 \div 10 = $ [ ]   c. $41 \div 2 = $ [ ]

b. $33 \div 4 = $ [ ]   d. $64 \div 5 = $ [ ]

3 Tanya has £140. She wants to buy some cassette tapes at £12 each. How many can she buy?  [ ]

4 Mrs Murphy is building shelves for her books. Each shelf holds 36 books and she has 150 books. How many shelves will she need?  [ ]

5 180 people have booked seats on a coach to go to the beach. Each coach holds 46 people. How many coaches will be needed?  [ ]

Activity sheet questions

Written

1–8
- Use doubling or halving, starting from known facts. For example:
  - double/halve any two-digit number by doubling/halving the tens first
  - double one number and halve the other
  - to multiply by 25, multiply by 100 then divide by 4
  - find the x16 table facts by doubling the x8 table
  - find sixths by halving thirds.

9–10
- Use factors (e.g. 8 x 12 = 8 x 4 x 3).
- Use closely related facts (e.g. multiply by 19 or 21 by multiplying by 20 and adjusting; develop the x12 table from the x10 and x2 tables).
- Partition (e.g. 47 x 6 = (40 x 6) + (7 x 6)).
- Use the relationship between multiplication and division.
- Use known facts and place value to multiply and divide mentally.

Teacher note

- Children need to adopt a systematic approach if all factors are to be found.

Answers

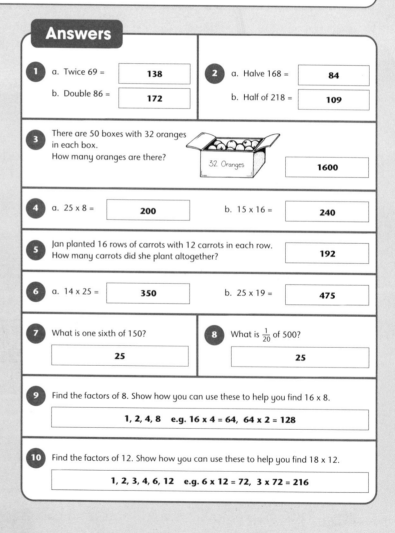

1
  a. Twice 69 =   **138**

  b. Double 86 =   **172**

2
  a. Halve 168 =   **84**

  b. Half of 218 =   **109**

3 There are 50 boxes with 32 oranges in each box.
How many oranges are there?

32 Oranges

   1600

4   a. 25 x 8 =   **200**   b. 15 x 16 =   **240**

5 Jan planted 16 rows of carrots with 12 carrots in each row.
How many carrots did she plant altogether?   **192**

6   a. 14 x 25 =   **350**   b. 25 x 19 =   **475**

7 What is one sixth of 150?   **25**

8 What is $\frac{1}{20}$ of 500?   **25**

9 Find the factors of 8. Show how you can use these to help you find 16 x 8.

   1, 2, 4, 8   e.g. 16 x 4 = 64, 64 x 2 = 128

10 Find the factors of 12. Show how you can use these to help you find 18 x 12.

   1, 2, 3, 4, 6, 12   e.g. 6 x 12 = 72, 3 x 72 = 216

Name: _____ Date: _____

1 a. Twice 69 = ⬚

b. Double 86 = ⬚

2 a. Halve 168 = ⬚

b. Half of 218 = ⬚

3 There are 50 boxes with 32 oranges in each box.
How many oranges are there?

32 Oranges

⬚

4 a. 25 x 8 = ⬚   b. 15 x 16 = ⬚

5 Jan planted 16 rows of carrots with 12 carrots in each row.
How many carrots did she plant altogether?

⬚

6 a. 14 x 25 = ⬚   b. 25 x 19= ⬚

7 What is one sixth of 150?

⬚

8 What is $\frac{1}{20}$ of 500?

⬚

9 Find the factors of 8. Show how you can use these to help you find 16 x 8.

⬚

10 Find the factors of 12. Show how you can use these to help you find 18 x 12.

⬚

Activity sheet questions

- Use doubling or halving, starting from known facts. For example:
  - double/halve any two-digit number by doubling/halving the tens first
  - double one number and halve the other
  - to multiply by 25, multiply by 100 then divide by 4
  - find the x16 table facts by doubling the x8 table
  - find sixths by halving thirds.
- Use factors (e.g. 8 x 12 = 8 x 4 x 3).

Oral
1–10
- Use known facts and place value to multiply and divide mentally.

Written
1–3
- Use closely related facts (e.g. multiply by 19 or 21 by multiplying by 20 and adjusting; develop the x12 table from the x10 and x2 tables).

4
- Partition (e.g. 47 x 6 = (40 x 6) + (7 x 6)).

5–6
- Use the relationship between multiplication and division.

Teacher note

- Emphasise the link between partitioning and any work the children have done involving the distributive law.

Oral questions

1. What is the product of 20 and 300?
2. Multiply 800 by 40.
3. 5400 divided by 10.
4. 3600 divided by 100.
5. 7800 divided by 1000.
6. Double 235.
7. Halve 300.
8. 30 times 8.
9. 400 lots of 6 equals how many?
10. 27 multiplied by 3.

Answers

1.	6000	6.	470
2.	32 000	7.	150
3.	540	8.	240
4.	36	9.	2400
5.	7.8	10.	81

1 Answer these questions.

a. 12 x 6 = 72   b. 9 x 12 = 108

2 a. 15 x 19 = 285   b. 19 x 26 = 494

3 a. 16 x 21 = 336   b. 21 x 15 = 315

4 a. 32 x 4 = 128   b. 47 x 5 = 235

5 What other number sentences can you write with these numbers? 72 ÷ 8 = 9

72 ÷ 9 = 8, 8 x 9 = 72, 9 x 8 = 72

6 Use the numbers 8, 12 and 96 to write four multiplication or division sentences.

8 x 12 = 96, 12 x 8 = 96, 96 ÷ 12 = 8, 96 ÷ 8 = 12

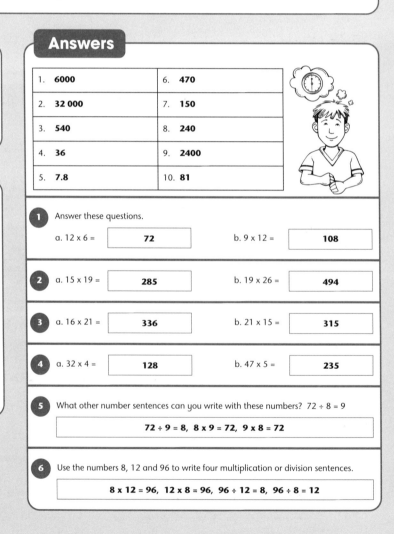

Name: _____   Date: _____

ASSESSMENT 17 — Mental calculation strategies (x and ÷)

1.	6.
2.	7.
3.	8.
4.	9.
5.	10.

1 Answer these questions.

a. $12 \times 6 = $ [   ]   b. $9 \times 12 = $ [   ]

2 a. $15 \times 19 = $ [   ]   b. $19 \times 26 = $ [   ]

3 a. $16 \times 21 = $ [   ]   b. $21 \times 15 = $ [   ]

4 a. $32 \times 4 = $ [   ]   b. $47 \times 5 = $ [   ]

5 What other number sentences can you write with these numbers? $72 \div 8 = 9$

[   ]

Use the numbers 8, 12 and 96 to write four multiplication or division sentences.

[   ]

Pencil and paper procedures (x and ÷)

Activity sheet questions

Written ● **Extend written methods to:**
- short multiplication of:

1–2   TU by U

3–5   HTU by U

6–8   U.t by U
- long multiplication of TU by TU
- short division of HTU by U (with integer remainder).

Teacher note

● The area method of multiplication allows children to utilise familiar facts and also emphasises place value.

Answers

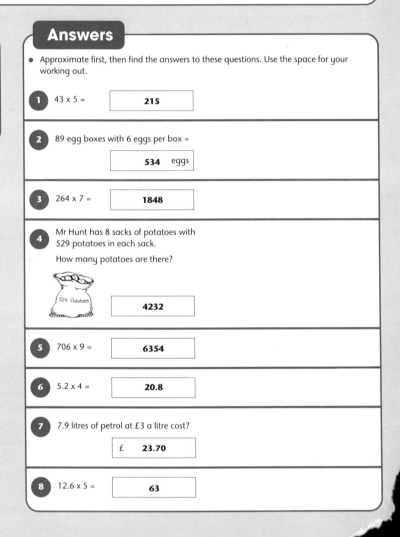

● Approximate first, then find the answers to these questions. Use the space for your working out.

1 43 × 5 = | **215** |

2 89 egg boxes with 6 eggs per box = | **534**   eggs |

3 264 × 7 = | **1848** |

4 Mr Hunt has 8 sacks of potatoes with 529 potatoes in each sack.

How many potatoes are there?

529 Potatoes | **4232** |

5 706 × 9 = | **6354** |

6 5.2 × 4 = | **20.8** |

7 7.9 litres of petrol at £3 a litre cost?   £ | **23.70** |

8 12.6 × 5 = | **63** |

Name: _____   Date: _____

Pencil and paper procedures (x and ÷)

● Approximate first, then find the answers to these questions. Use the space for your working out.

1   43 x 5 =   [   ]

2   89 egg boxes with 6 eggs per box =

[   ] eggs

3   264 x 7 =   [   ]

4   Mr Hunt has 8 sacks of potatoes with 529 potatoes in each sack.

How many potatoes are there?

529 Potatoes

[   ]

5   706 x 9 =   [   ]

6   5.2 x 4 =   [   ]

7   7.9 litres of petrol at £3 a litre cost?

£ [   ]

8   12.6 x 5 =   [   ]

Activity sheet questions

Written ● Extend written methods to:

1–4
- short multiplication of TU by U, HTU by U or U.t by U
- long multiplication of TU by TU

5–7
- short division of HTU by U (with integer remainder).

Teacher note

● The area method of multiplication can be developed for more complex calculations.

Answers

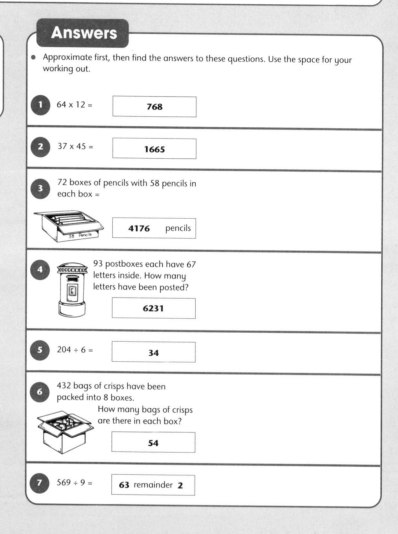

● Approximate first, then find the answers to these questions. Use the space for your working out.

1 64 x 12 = ☐ **768**

2 37 x 45 = ☐ **1665**

3 72 boxes of pencils with 58 pencils in each box =

☐ **4176** pencils

4 93 postboxes each have 67 letters inside. How many letters have been posted?

☐ **6231**

5 204 ÷ 6 = ☐ **34**

6 432 bags of crisps have been packed into 8 boxes.

How many bags of crisps are there in each box?

☐ **54**

7 569 ÷ 9 = ☐ **63** remainder **2**

Pencil and paper procedures (x and ÷)

- Approximate first, then find the answers to these questions. Use the space for your working out.

1   64 x 12 =

2   37 x 45 =

3   72 boxes of pencils with 58 pencils in each box =

   pencils

4   93 postboxes each have 67 letters inside. How many letters have been posted?

5   204 ÷ 6 =

6   432 bags of crisps have been packed into 8 boxes.
How many bags of crisps are there in each box?

7   569 ÷ 9 =   remainder

Activity sheet questions

Written

1–6
- Solve mathematical problems or puzzles, recognise and explain patterns and relationships, generalise and predict.
  Suggest extensions asking 'What if …?'
- Make and investigate a general statement about familiar numbers or shapes by finding examples that satisfy it.
  Explain a generalised relationship (formula) in words.

Teacher note

- These questions emphasise the using and applying aspects of mathematics, including simplifying, being systematic, generalising, trial and error, interpreting, etc. These are the abilities that allow children to make use of their mathematics in context. Many children who can successfully multiply, for example, have difficulty when faced with a multiplication question in problem form, often because of an inability to organise their thinking sufficiently. The abilities of simplifying, being systematic, etc. develop through repeated experiences of situations that require these.

Answers

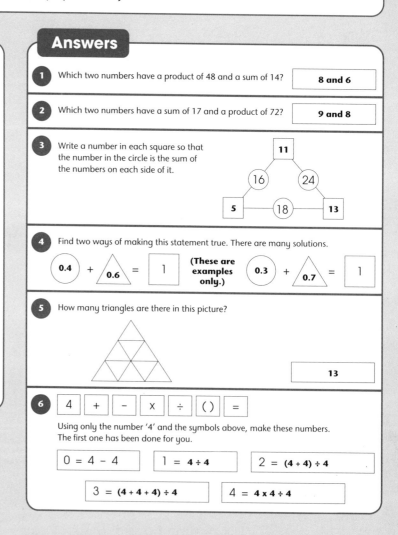

1 Which two numbers have a product of 48 and a sum of 14?   **8 and 6**

2 Which two numbers have a sum of 17 and a product of 72?   **9 and 8**

3 Write a number in each square so that the number in the circle is the sum of the numbers on each side of it.

11 / 16 / 24 / 5 / 18 / 13

4 Find two ways of making this statement true. There are many solutions.

0.4 + 0.6 = 1   (These are examples only.)   0.3 + 0.7 = 1

5 How many triangles are there in this picture?   **13**

6 4 + – x ÷ ( ) =

Using only the number '4' and the symbols above, make these numbers. The first one has been done for you.

0 = 4 – 4   1 = 4 ÷ 4   2 = (4 + 4) ÷ 4

3 = (4 + 4 + 4) ÷ 4   4 = 4 x 4 ÷ 4

Name: _____ Date: _____

1 Which two numbers have a product of 48 and a sum of 14? [   ]

2 Which two numbers have a sum of 17 and a product of 72? [   ]

3 Write a number in each square so that the number in the circle is the sum of the numbers on each side of it.

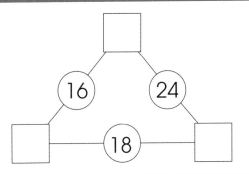

4 Find two ways of making this statement true. There are many solutions.

◯ + △ = [1]   ◯ + △ = [1]

5 How many triangles are there in this picture?

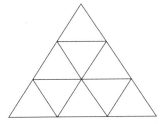

[   ]

6 [4] [+] [−] [x] [÷] [( )] [=]

Using only the number '4' and the symbols above, make these numbers. The first one has been done for you.

[0 = 4 − 4]   [1 =]   [2 =]

[3 =]   [4 =]

21 Reasoning and generalising about numbers or shapes

Activity sheet questions

● Solve mathematical problems or puzzles, recognise and explain patterns and relationships, generalise and predict.
Suggest extensions asking 'What if …?'

Written 1-6

● **Make and investigate a general statement about familiar numbers or shapes by finding examples that satisfy it.**
Explain a generalised relationship (formula) in words.

Teacher note

● These generalised statements require a good degree of understanding about numbers if they are to be tackled successfully. Children need to develop the habit of considering more than one example in support of their conclusion.

Answers

● Write 'True' or 'False' next to each statement. Give one or two examples to explain your answer.

1 Multiplying whole numbers together gives a larger answer. — **True**

e.g. 3 x 4 = 12, 70 x 3 = 210

2 It does not matter which way round you do subtraction. — **False**

e.g. 35 – 14 = 21, 14 – 35 = –21; 5 – 4 = 1, 4 – 5 = –1

3 A multiple of 9 is always a multiple of 3. — **True**

e.g 18 ÷ 9 = 2, 18 ÷ 3 = 6; 36 ÷ 9 = 4, 36 ÷ 3 = 12

4 The sum of three consecutive numbers is always odd. — **False**

e.g. 1 + 2 + 3 = 6

5 All pentagons have 5 obtuse angles. — **False**

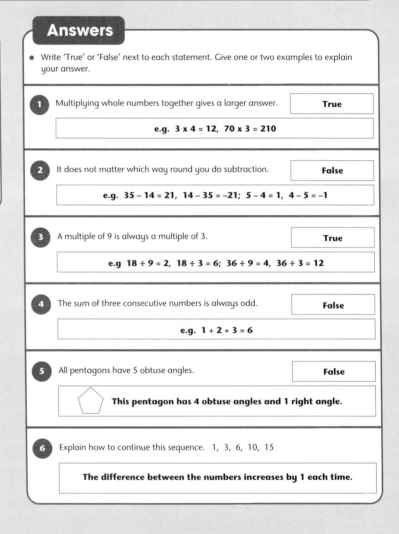 This pentagon has 4 obtuse angles and 1 right angle.

6 Explain how to continue this sequence. 1, 3, 6, 10, 15

The difference between the numbers increases by 1 each time.

Name: _____   Date: _____

21 Reasoning and generalising about numbers or shapes

- Write 'True' or 'False' next to each statement. Give one or two examples to explain your answer.

1 Multiplying whole numbers together gives a larger answer.

2 It does not matter which way round you do subtraction.

3 A multiple of 9 is always a multiple of 3.

4 The sum of three consecutive numbers is always odd.

5 All pentagons have 5 obtuse angles.

6 Explain how to continue this sequence.   1, 3, 6, 10, 15

Activity sheet questions

Written

1-7
- Use all four operations to solve simple word problems involving numbers and quantities based on 'real life', money and measures (including time), using one or more steps, including making simple conversions of pounds to foreign currency and finding simple percentages.

Explain methods and reasoning.

Teacher note

- Children often incorrectly write five pounds and eight pence as £5.8, £5.8p or £5.08p rather than £5.08 or 508p.

Current year	Popocatepetl	Llullaillaco
1999	56 years	122 years
2000	57 years	123 years
2001	58 years	124 years
2002	59 years	125 years
2003	60 years	126 years

Answers

This table shows the names, eruption dates and heights in metres of some volcanoes.

Name	Height(m)	Last eruption
Mount St Helens	2549	1988
Etna	3350	1992
Popocatepetl	5465	1943
Mauna Loa	4170	1984
Llullaillaco	6723	1877

- Answer these questions.

1 How much higher is Mauna Loa than Mount St Helens? **1621m**

2 What is the difference in height between Popocatepetl and Etna? **2115m**

3 How long ago did these volcanoes last erupt? **(See table opposite for answers.)**

a. Popocatepetl [ ]   b. Llullaillaco [ ]

4 How many years after Llullaillaco's last eruption was the last eruption of Mount St Helens? **111 years**

5 What change do you get for a CD that costs £12.49 if you pay £20? **£7.51**

6 A pint of milk costs 38p. How much would it cost to fill an 8 pint jug? **£3.04**

7 There is 10% off the prices in a sale. What is the new price of something that originially cost £5? **£4.50**

Name: _____ Date: _____

This table shows the names, eruption dates and heights in metres of some volcanoes.

Name	Height(m)	Last eruption
Mount St Helens	2549	1988
Etna	3350	1992
Popocatepetl	5465	1943
Mauna Loa	4170	1984
Llullaillaco	6723	1877

● Answer these questions.

1 How much higher is Mauna Loa than Mount St Helens? [   ]

2 What is the difference in height between Popocatepetl and Etna? [   ]

3 How long ago did these volcanoes last erupt?

a. Popocatepetl [   ]   b. Llullaillaco [   ]

4 How many years after Llullaillaco's last eruption was the last eruption of Mount St Helens? [   ]

5 What change do you get for a CD that costs £12.49 if you pay £20? [   ]

6 A pint of milk costs 38p. How much would it cost to fill an 8 pint jug? [   ]

7 There is 10% off the prices in a sale. What is the new price of something that originally cost £5? [   ]

Activity sheet questions

Written
1–6
● Use all four operations to solve simple word problems involving numbers and quantities based on 'real life', money and measures (including time), using one or more steps, including making simple conversions of pounds to foreign currency and finding simple percentages.
Explain methods and reasoning.

Teacher note

● Children often find relatively simple calculations difficult when they are placed in context. Such questions demand abilities in addition to those required to do the calculation, e.g. interpretation, reasoning, extracting the relevant information, etc.

Answers

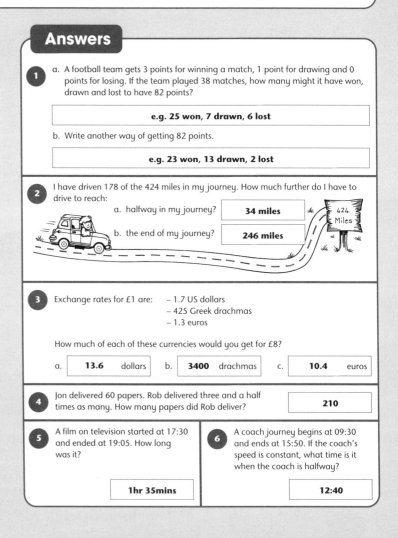

1
a. A football team gets 3 points for winning a match, 1 point for drawing and 0 points for losing. If the team played 38 matches, how many might it have won, drawn and lost to have 82 points?

> **e.g. 25 won, 7 drawn, 6 lost**

b. Write another way of getting 82 points.

> **e.g. 23 won, 13 drawn, 2 lost**

2 I have driven 178 of the 424 miles in my journey. How much further do I have to drive to reach:
a. halfway in my journey? **34 miles**
b. the end of my journey? **246 miles**

424 Miles

3 Exchange rates for £1 are: – 1.7 US dollars
– 425 Greek drachmas
– 1.3 euros

How much of each of these currencies would you get for £8?

a. **13.6** dollars   b. **3400** drachmas   c. **10.4** euros

4 Jon delivered 60 papers. Rob delivered three and a half times as many. How many papers did Rob deliver?   **210**

5 A film on television started at 17:30 and ended at 19:05. How long was it?

1hr 35mins

6 A coach journey begins at 09:30 and ends at 15:50. If the coach's speed is constant, what time is it when the coach is halfway?

12:40

Name: _____ Date: _____

1

a. A football team gets 3 points for winning a match, 1 point for drawing and 0 points for losing. If the team played 38 matches, how many might it have won, drawn and lost to have 82 points?

b. Write another way of getting 82 points.

2 I have driven 178 of the 424 miles in my journey. How much further do I have to drive to reach:

a. halfway in my journey?

b. the end of my journey?

424 Miles

3 Exchange rates for £1 are:
– 1.7 US dollars
– 425 Greek drachmas
– 1.3 euros

How much of each of these currencies would you get for £8?

a. _____ dollars   b. _____ drachmas   c. _____ euros

4 Jon delivered 60 papers. Rob delivered three and a half times as many. How many papers did Rob deliver?

5 A film on television started at 17:30 and ended at 19:05. How long was it?

6 A coach journey begins at 09:30 and ends at 15:50. If the coach's speed is constant, what time is it when the coach is halfway?

ASSESSMENT 24 Handling data

Activity sheet questions

Written

1–10
- Solve a problem by representing and interpreting data in tables, charts, graphs and diagrams, including those generated by computer, for example: bar line charts, vertical axis labelled in 2s, 5s, 10s, 20s or 100s, first where intermediate points have no meaning (e.g. scores on a dice rolled 50 times), then where they may have meaning (e.g. room temperature over time).

3
- Find the mode of a set of data.

7–8
- Discuss the chance or likelihood of particular events.

Teacher note

- Children often fail to realise that they can find the total number of people being questioned straight from the graph by adding the values of each bar.
- The mode is the value that occurs most frequently in a set of data.

Answers

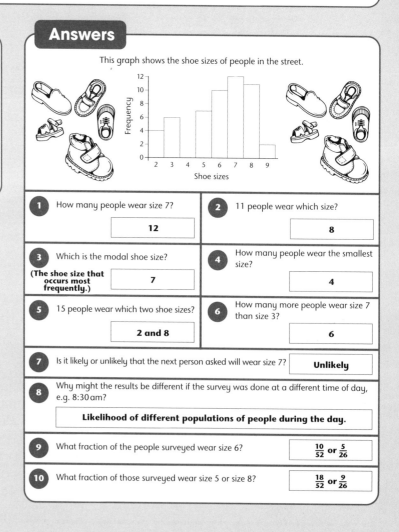

This graph shows the shoe sizes of people in the street.

1 How many people wear size 7?
12

2 11 people wear which size?
8

3 Which is the modal shoe size?
(The shoe size that occurs most frequently.)
7

4 How many people wear the smallest size?
4

5 15 people wear which two shoe sizes?
2 and 8

6 How many more people wear size 7 than size 3?
6

7 Is it likely or unlikely that the next person asked will wear size 7?
Unlikely

8 Why might the results be different if the survey was done at a different time of day, e.g. 8:30 am?
Likelihood of different populations of people during the day.

9 What fraction of the people surveyed wear size 6?
$\frac{10}{52}$ or $\frac{5}{26}$

10 What fraction of those surveyed wear size 5 or size 8?
$\frac{18}{52}$ or $\frac{9}{26}$

Name: _____   Date: _____

Handling data

This graph shows the shoe sizes of people in the street.

Frequency (y-axis: 0, 2, 4, 6, 8, 10, 12)
Shoe sizes (x-axis: 2, 3, 4, 5, 6, 7, 8, 9)

1 How many people wear size 7?

2 11 people wear which size?

3 Which is the modal shoe size?

4 How many people wear the smallest size?

5 15 people wear which two shoe sizes?

6 How many more people wear size 7 than size 3?

7 Is it likely or unlikely that the next person asked will wear size 7?

8 Why might the results be different if the survey was done at a different time of day, e.g. 8:30 am?

9 What fraction of the people surveyed wear size 6?

10 What fraction of those surveyed wear size 5 or size 8?

© Folens (copiable page)   MATHS WEEKLY ASSESSMENT: *Book 5*   51

Handling data

ASSESSMENT 25

Activity sheet questions

- Discuss the chance or likelihood of particular events.

Written 1–7

- Solve a problem by representing and interpreting data in tables, charts, graphs and diagrams, including those generated by computer, for example: bar line charts, vertical axis labelled in 2s, 5s, 10s, 20s or 100s, first where intermediate points have no meaning (e.g. scores on a dice rolled 50 times), then where they may have meaning (e.g. room temperature over time).
- Find the mode of a set of data.

Teacher note

- Children need to realise that, unlike on this graph, intermediate points on a line graph may be meaningless, e.g. on a graph showing the results of rolling a dice, where a roll of $5\frac{1}{2}$ is impossible.

Answers

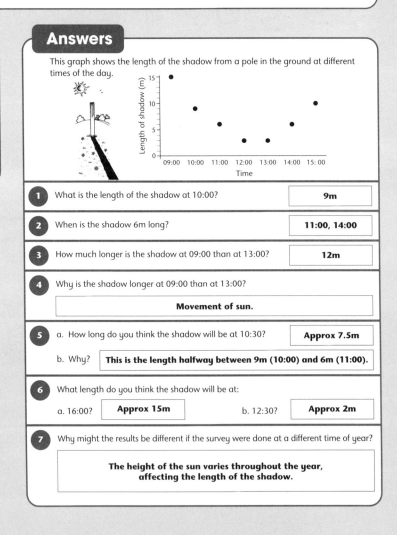

This graph shows the length of the shadow from a pole in the ground at different times of the day.

| 1 | What is the length of the shadow at 10:00? | **9m** |

| 2 | When is the shadow 6m long? | **11:00, 14:00** |

| 3 | How much longer is the shadow at 09:00 than at 13:00? | **12m** |

4	Why is the shadow longer at 09:00 than at 13:00?
	Movement of sun.

| 5 | a. How long do you think the shadow will be at 10:30? | **Approx 7.5m** |

b. Why? | **This is the length halfway between 9m (10:00) and 6m (11:00).**

| 6 | What length do you think the shadow will be at: |
| | a. 16:00? **Approx 15m**   b. 12:30? **Approx 2m** |

7	Why might the results be different if the survey were done at a different time of year?
	The height of the sun varies throughout the year, affecting the length of the shadow.

52

Name: _____   Date: _____

This graph shows the length of the shadow from a pole in the ground at different times of the day.

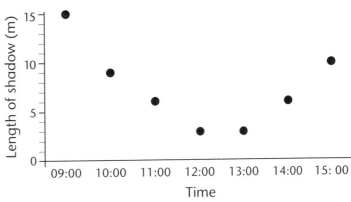

1 What is the length of the shadow at 10:00?

2 When is the shadow 6m long?

3 How much longer is the shadow at 09:00 than at 13:00?

4 Why is the shadow longer at 09:00 than at 13:00?

5 a. How long do you think the shadow will be at 10:30?

b. Why?

6 What length do you think the shadow will be at:

a. 16:00?   b. 12:30?

7 Why might the results be different if the survey were done at a different time of year?

Handling data

Activity sheet questions

Oral 1–10 and Written 1

- ● Discuss the chance or likelihood of particular events.
- ○ Solve a problem by representing and interpreting data in tables, charts, graphs and diagrams, including those generated by computer, for example: bar line charts, vertical axis labelled in 2s, 5s, 10s, 20s or 100s, first where intermediate points have no meaning (e.g. scores on a dice rolled 50 times), then where they may have meaning (e.g. room temperature over time).

2–5
- ● Find the mode and range of a set of data.

Teacher note

- ● It is possible to have more than one mode for a set of data, as in 6, 7, 7, 7, 8, 9, 9, 9, 10.

Oral questions

On the board write the words, **Impossible, Unlikely, Even chance, Likely, Certain.** Begin the test by saying, 'Write one of these words for each question'.

1. The day after Monday will be Thursday.
2. It will get dark tonight.
3. It will rain during April.
4. When you toss a coin the result will be heads.
5. When a dice is rolled you will get a number less than 5.
6. You will get a picture card when you pick from a pack of cards.
7. When you toss a coin 20 times you will get 15 heads.
8. You will get a red card when you pick a card from a pack of cards.
9. When a dice is rolled you will get a number greater than 3.
10. I will win an Olympic medal.

Answers

1.	**Impossible**	6.	**Unlikely**
2.	**Certain**	7.	**Unlikely**
3.	**Likely**	8.	**Even chance**
4.	**Even chance**	9.	**Even chance**
5.	**Likely**	10.	**Unlikely**

1 Join each statement to the line.

impossible   poor chance   even chance   good chance   certain

The next car I see will have a 4 in the number plate.

There will be 8 days in the week this week.

If I rolled a dice 20 times I would get at least one 6.

2 Write the mode of this list of numbers.
1, 2, 2, 4, 5, 5, 6, 6 ,6, 7

6

3 Write the mode of this list of numbers.
8, 4, 6, 8, 1, 3, 9, 3, 8, 4, 9

8

4 These are the heights of some pupils in a class. Which is the modal height?

1.27m, 1.34m, 1.31m, 1.27m, 1.34m, 1.31m, 1.27m

1.27m

5 What is the range of the numbers in:

a. question 2?   **6**   b. question 3?   **8**

Name: _____ Date: _____

1.	6.
2.	7.
3.	8.
4.	9.
5.	10.

1 Join each statement to the line.

impossible   poor chance   even chance   good chance   certain

_____

| The next car I see will have a 4 in the number plate. | There will be 8 days in the week this week. | If I rolled a dice 20 times I would get at least one 6. |

2 Write the mode of this list of numbers.
1, 2, 2, 4, 5, 5, 6, 6 ,6, 7

3 Write the mode of this list of numbers.
8, 4, 6, 8, 1, 3, 9, 3, 8, 4, 9

4 These are the heights of some pupils in a class. Which is the modal height?

1.27m, 1.34m, 1.31m, 1.27m, 1.34m, 1.31m, 1.27m

5 What is the range of the numbers in:

a. question 2?

b. question 3?

Activity sheet questions

Oral
1–10
- Use, read and write standard metric units (km, m, cm, mm, kg, g, l, ml), including their abbreviations, and relationships between them.
Convert larger to smaller units (e.g. km to m, m to cm or mm, kg to g, l to ml).
Know imperial units (mile, pint, gallon).

Written
1–3
- Suggest suitable units and measuring equipment to estimate or measure length, mass or capacity.
4 Record estimates and readings from scales to a suitable degree of accuracy.
5 Measure and draw lines to the nearest millimetre.
- Understand area measured in square centimetres (cm^2).
Understand and use the formula in words 'length x breadth' for the area of a rectangle.
Understand, measure and calculate perimeters of rectangles and regular polygons.
- Use units of time; read the time on a 24-hour digital clock and use 24-hour clock notation, such as 19:53.
Use timetables.

Teacher note

- Remind children that we do not put a full stop or an 's' on the end of km, m, cm, mm, kg, g, l, ml (as in 3kg. or 3kgs).
- Children will require a ruler for the written questions.

Oral questions

1. Write the abbreviation for kilometre.
2. What does ml stand for?
3. Write the abbreviation for square centimetres
4. Is a mile more or less than a km?
5. Which is more: $\frac{1}{2}$ a litre or a pint?
6. One hundredth of a metre is?
7. What fraction of 1kg is 10g?
8. Write 2.4m in centimetres.
9. Write 4.5 litres in millilitres.
10. Write 143mm in centimetres.

Answers

1.	km	6.	1cm
2.	millilitre(s)	7.	$\frac{1}{100}$ kg
3.	cm^2	8.	240cm
4.	More	9.	4500ml
5.	Pint	10.	14.3cm

1 Suggest something you would measure in: (These are examples only.)
- a. metres — Length of a classroom
- b. litres — Lemonade
- c. pints — Milk/beer
- d. kilograms — My weight
- e. millimetres — Length of a fingernail
- f. grams — Cooking ingredients

2 Which unit might you use to measure these.
- a. Length of a car — Metres
- b. A car journey — Miles or kilometres
- c. Width of a television — Centimetres
- d. Weight of an apple — Grams

3 Tick the statement you think is correct.
- a. The height of our classroom door is about: 1m ☐ 2m ✓ 3m ☐
- b. The capacity of a bucket is about: 0.8l ☐ 8l ✓ 80l ☐

4 How much are these scales showing?
- a. 10kg
- b. 300g or 0.3kg

5 How long are these lines in mm? a. _____ 56mm
b. _____ 78mm

Name: _____   Date: _____

Measures

1.	6.
2.	7.
3.	8.
4.	9.
5.	10.

1 Suggest something you would measure in:

a. metres ☐

b. litres ☐

c. pints ☐

d. kilograms ☐

e. millimetres ☐

f. grams ☐

2 Which unit might you use to measure these.

a. Length of a car ☐

b. A car journey ☐

c. Width of a television ☐

d. Weight of an apple ☐

3 Tick the statement you think is correct.

a. The height of our classroom door is about: 1m ☐   2m ☐   3m ☐

b. The capacity of a bucket is about: 0.8l ☐   8l ☐   80l ☐

4 How much are these scales showing?

a.   4   8   12kg

b.   0   1kg

5 How long are these lines in mm?   a. _____ ☐

b. _____ ☐

Activity sheet questions

- Use, read and write standard metric units (km, m, cm, mm, kg, g, l, ml), including their abbreviations, and relationships between them.
  Convert larger to smaller units (e.g. km to m, m to cm or mm, kg to g, l to ml).
  Know imperial units (mile, pint, gallon).
- Suggest suitable units and measuring equipment to estimate or measure length, mass or capacity.
  Measure and draw lines to the nearest millimetre.
  Record estimates and readings from scales to a suitable degree of accuracy.

Written 1–7
- **Understand area measured in square centimetres (cm²).**
  Understand and use the formula in words 'length x breadth' for the area of a rectangle.
  Understand, measure and calculate perimeters of rectangles and regular polygons.
- Use units of time; read the time on a 24-hour digital clock and use 24-hour clock notation, such as 19:53.
  Use timetables.

Teacher note

- Children often confuse area and perimeter. This can result in moving too quickly to the formula l x b for finding area with insufficient time given to developing a sense of what area is. This means that both area and perimeter are found by using the lengths of the sides only, in the case of rectangles by adding 4 of them or multiplying 2.
- Children will require a ruler for this assessment.

Answers

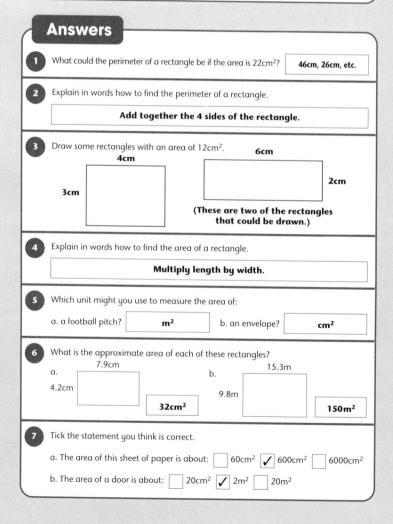

1. What could the perimeter of a rectangle be if the area is 22cm²? **46cm, 26cm, etc.**

2. Explain in words how to find the perimeter of a rectangle.
   Add together the 4 sides of the rectangle.

3. Draw some rectangles with an area of 12cm².
   4cm / 3cm   6cm / 2cm
   (These are two of the rectangles that could be drawn.)

4. Explain in words how to find the area of a rectangle.
   Multiply length by width.

5. Which unit might you use to measure the area of:
   a. a football pitch? **m²**   b. an envelope? **cm²**

6. What is the approximate area of each of these rectangles?
   a. 7.9cm / 4.2cm **32cm²**   b. 15.3m / 9.8m **150m²**

7. Tick the statement you think is correct.
   a. The area of this sheet of paper is about: ☐ 60cm² ☑ 600cm² ☐ 6000cm²
   b. The area of a door is about: ☐ 20cm² ☑ 2m² ☐ 20m²

Name: _____ Date: _____

Measures

1 What could the perimeter of a rectangle be if the area is 22cm²? [   ]

2 Explain in words how to find the perimeter of a rectangle.

[   ]

3 Draw some rectangles with an area of 12cm².

4 Explain in words how to find the area of a rectangle.

[   ]

5 Which unit might you use to measure the area of:

a. a football pitch? [   ] b. an envelope? [   ]

6 What is the approximate area of each of these rectangles?

a.
7.9cm
4.2cm
[   ]
[   ]

b.
15.3m
9.8m
[   ]
[   ]

7 Tick the statement you think is correct.

a. The area of this sheet of paper is about: [ ] 60cm² [ ] 600cm² [ ] 6000cm²

b. The area of a door is about: [ ] 20cm² [ ] 2m² [ ] 20m²

Activity sheet questions

- Use, read and write standard metric units (km, m, cm, mm, kg, g, l, ml), including their abbreviations, and relationships between them.
  Convert larger to smaller units (e.g. km to m, m to cm or mm, kg to g, l to ml).
  Know imperial units (mile, pint, gallon).
- Suggest suitable units and measuring equipment to estimate or measure length, mass or capacity.
  Measure and draw lines to the nearest millimetre.
  Record estimates and readings from scales to a suitable degree of accuracy.
- Understand area measured in square centimetres (cm²).
  Understand and use the formula in words 'length x breadth' for the area of a rectangle.
  Understand, measure and calculate perimeters of rectangles and regular polygons.

Written

1–3
- Use units of time;

4–5
  read the time on a 24-hour digital clock and use 24-hour clock notation, such as 19:53.

6
  Use timetables.

Teacher note

- Note that four digits are always used in the 24-hour clock, e.g. 05:15, 19:34, 20:00.

Answers

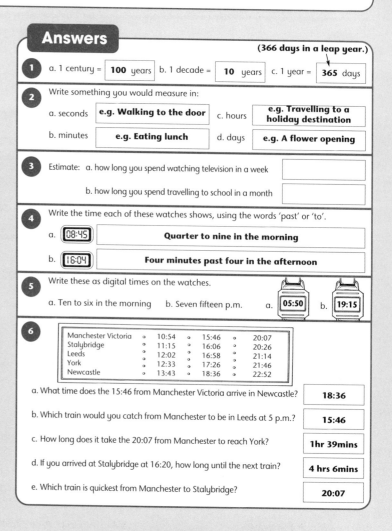

(366 days in a leap year.)

1 a. 1 century = **100** years   b. 1 decade = **10** years   c. 1 year = **365** days

2 Write something you would measure in:

a. seconds | **e.g. Walking to the door** | c. hours | **e.g. Travelling to a holiday destination**
b. minutes | **e.g. Eating lunch** | d. days | **e.g. A flower opening**

3 Estimate: a. how long you spend watching television in a week

b. how long you spend travelling to school in a month

4 Write the time each of these watches shows, using the words 'past' or 'to'.

a. 08:45   **Quarter to nine in the morning**

b. 16:04   **Four minutes past four in the afternoon**

5 Write these as digital times on the watches.

a. Ten to six in the morning   b. Seven fifteen p.m.   a. **05:50**   b. **19:15**

6

Manchester Victoria	○	10:54	○	15:46	○	20:07
Stalybridge	○	11:15	○	16:06	○	20:26
Leeds	○	12:02	○	16:58	○	21:14
York	○	12:33	○	17:26	○	21:46
Newcastle	○	13:43	○	18:36	○	22:52

a. What time does the 15:46 from Manchester Victoria arrive in Newcastle?   **18:36**

b. Which train would you catch from Manchester to be in Leeds at 5 p.m.?   **15:46**

c. How long does it take the 20:07 from Manchester to reach York?   **1hr 39mins**

d. If you arrived at Stalybridge at 16:20, how long until the next train?   **4 hrs 6mins**

e. Which train is quickest from Manchester to Stalybridge?   **20:07**

Name: _____ Date: _____

1 a. 1 century = [___] years b. 1 decade = [___] years c. 1 year = [___] days

2 Write something you would measure in:

a. seconds [___]   c. hours [___]

b. minutes [___]   d. days [___]

3 Estimate: a. how long you spend watching television in a week [___]

b. how long you spend travelling to school in a month [___]

4 Write the time each of these watches shows, using the words 'past' or 'to'.

a. [08:45] [___]

b. [16:04] [___]

5 Write these as digital times on the watches.

a. Ten to six in the morning   b. Seven fifteen p.m.   a. [___]   b. [___]

6

Manchester Victoria	10:54	15:46	20:07
Stalybridge	11:15	16:06	20:26
Leeds	12:02	16:58	21:14
York	12:33	17:26	21:46
Newcastle	13:43	18:36	22:52

a. What time does the 15:46 from Manchester Victoria arrive in Newcastle? [___]

b. Which train would you catch from Manchester to be in Leeds at 5 p.m.? [___]

c. How long does it take the 20:07 from Manchester to reach York? [___]

d. If you arrived at Stalybridge at 16:20, how long until the next train? [___]

e. Which train is quickest from Manchester to Stalybridge? [___]

Activity sheet questions

Written 1–3

- Recognise properties of rectangles.
- **Classify triangles (isosceles, equilateral, scalene), using criteria such as equal sides, equal angles, lines of symmetry.**
- Classify solid shapes.
- Make shapes with increasing accuracy.
  Visualise 3D shapes from 2D drawings and identify different nets for an open cube.
- Recognise reflective symmetry in regular polygons: for example, know that a square has four axes of symmetry and an equilateral triangle has three.
  Complete symmetrical patterns with two lines of symmetry at right angles (using squared paper or pegboard).
  Recognise where a shape will be after reflection in a mirror line parallel to one side (sides not all parallel or perpendicular to the mirror line).
  Recognise where a shape will be after a translation.
- Recognise positions and directions:
  – read and plot co-ordinates in the first quadrant
  – recognise perpendicular and parallel lines.
- Understand and use angle measure in degrees.
  Identify, estimate and order acute and obtuse angles.
  Use a protractor to measure and draw acute and obtuse angles to the nearest 5°.
  Calculate angles in a straight line.

Teacher note

- Children need to see a varied range of drawings of triangles to avoid misconceptions developing, e.g. the belief that triangles have a horizontal base.
- Children will require a ruler for this assessment.

Answers

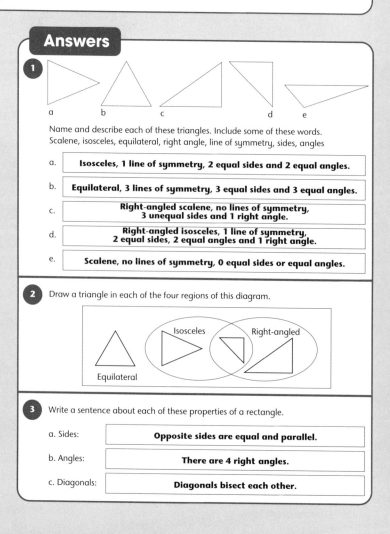

1

a   b   c   d   e

Name and describe each of these triangles. Include some of these words.
Scalene, isosceles, equilateral, right angle, line of symmetry, sides, angles

a. **Isosceles, 1 line of symmetry, 2 equal sides and 2 equal angles.**

b. **Equilateral, 3 lines of symmetry, 3 equal sides and 3 equal angles.**

c. **Right-angled scalene, no lines of symmetry, 3 unequal sides and 1 right angle.**

d. **Right-angled isosceles, 1 line of symmetry, 2 equal sides, 2 equal angles and 1 right angle.**

e. **Scalene, no lines of symmetry, 0 equal sides or equal angles.**

2 Draw a triangle in each of the four regions of this diagram.

Isosceles   Right-angled

Equilateral

3 Write a sentence about each of these properties of a rectangle.

a. Sides: **Opposite sides are equal and parallel.**

b. Angles: **There are 4 right angles.**

c. Diagonals: **Diagonals bisect each other.**

Name: _____ Date: _____

1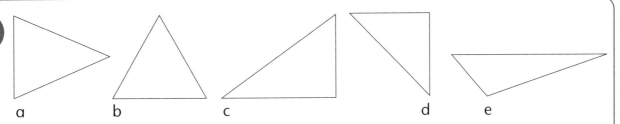

Name and describe each of these triangles. Include some of these words.
Scalene, isosceles, equilateral, right angle, line of symmetry, sides, angles

a. _____

b. _____

c. _____

d. _____

e. _____

2 Draw a triangle in each of the four regions of this diagram.

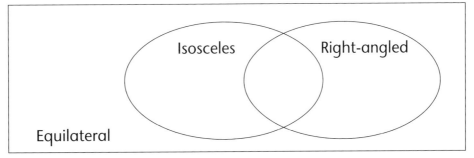

3 Write a sentence about each of these properties of a rectangle.

a. Sides: _____

b. Angles: _____

c. Diagonals: _____

Activity sheet questions

- Recognise properties of rectangles.
  Classify triangles (isosceles, equilateral, scalene), using criteria such as equal sides, equal angles, lines of symmetry.

Written
1–2, 4
3, 5
- **Classify solid shapes.**
- **Make shapes with increasing accuracy.**
  Visualise 3D shapes from 2D drawings and identify different nets for an open cube.

- Recognise reflective symmetry in regular polygons: for example, know that a square has four axes of symmetry and an equilateral triangle has three.
  Complete symmetrical patterns with two lines of symmetry at right angles (using squared paper or pegboard).
  Recognise where a shape will be after reflection in a mirror line parallel to one side (sides not all parallel or perpendicular to the mirror line).
  Recognise where a shape will be after a translation.

- Recognise positions and directions:
  – read and plot co-ordinates in the first quadrant
  – recognise perpendicular and parallel lines.

- Understand and use angle measure in degrees.
  Identify, estimate and order acute and obtuse angles.
  Use a protractor to measure and draw acute and obtuse angles to the nearest 5°.
  Calculate angles in a straight line.

Teacher note

- Children need access to solid shapes, without which they may think that a cube, for example, has only 9 edges because of its drawn picture.

Answers

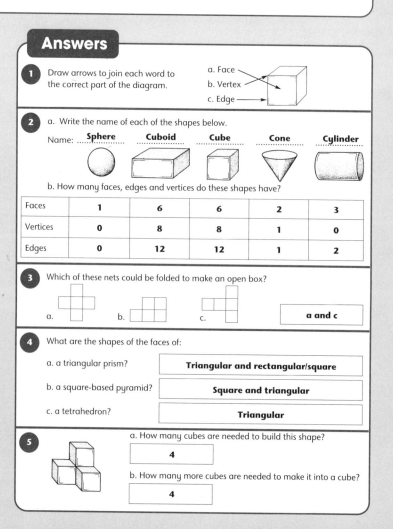

1 Draw arrows to join each word to the correct part of the diagram.
a. Face
b. Vertex
c. Edge

2 a. Write the name of each of the shapes below.

Name: **Sphere** **Cuboid** **Cube** **Cone** **Cylinder**

b. How many faces, edges and vertices do these shapes have?

Faces	1	6	6	2	3
Vertices	0	8	8	1	0
Edges	0	12	12	1	2

3 Which of these nets could be folded to make an open box?

a.   b.   c.   **a and c**

4 What are the shapes of the faces of:

a. a triangular prism?   **Triangular and rectangular/square**

b. a square-based pyramid?   **Square and triangular**

c. a tetrahedron?   **Triangular**

5 a. How many cubes are needed to build this shape?   **4**

b. How many more cubes are needed to make it into a cube?   **4**

Name: _____   Date: _____

 ASSESSMENT 31

Shape and space – 2D

1 Draw arrows to join each word to the correct part of the diagram.

a. Face

b. Vertex

c. Edge

2 a. Write the name of each of the shapes below.

Name: ....

b. How many faces, edges and vertices do these shapes have?

Faces					
Vertices					
Edges					

3 Which of these nets could be folded to make an open box?

a. b. c.

4 What are the shapes of the faces of:

a. a triangular prism?

b. a square-based pyramid?

c. a tetrahedron?

5 a. How many cubes are needed to build this shape?

b. How many more cubes are needed to make it into a cube?

Activity sheet questions

- Recognise properties of rectangles.
  Classify triangles (isosceles, equilateral, scalene), using criteria such as equal sides, equal angles, lines of symmetry.
- Classify solid shapes.
- Make shapes with increasing accuracy.
  Visualise 3D shapes from 2D drawings and identify different nets for an open cube.

Written

1–3
- **Recognise reflective symmetry in regular polygons: for example, know that a square has four axes of symmetry and an equilateral triangle has three.**

4
Complete symmetrical patterns with two lines of symmetry at right angles (using squared paper or pegboard).

5
Recognise where a shape will be after reflection in a mirror line parallel to one side (sides not all parallel or perpendicular to the mirror line).
Recognise where a shape will be after a translation.

- Recognise positions and directions:
  - read and plot co-ordinates in the first quadrant
  - recognise perpendicular and parallel lines.
- Understand and use angle measure in degrees.
  Identify, estimate and order acute and obtuse angles.
  Use a protractor to measure and draw acute and obtuse angles to the nearest 5°.
  Calculate angles in a straight line.

Teacher note

- Encourage children always to look for more than one line of symmetry.
- Children will require a ruler for this assessment.

Answers

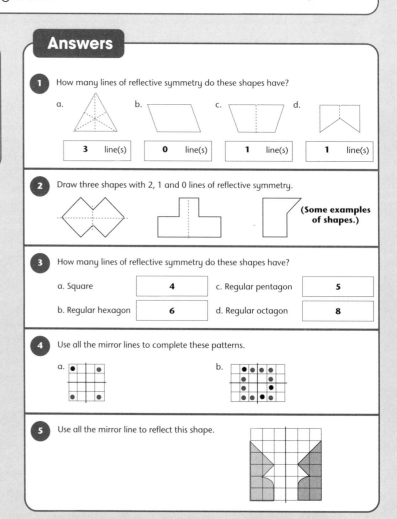

1 How many lines of reflective symmetry do these shapes have?

a. b. c. d.

| **3** line(s) | **0** line(s) | **1** line(s) | **1** line(s) |

2 Draw three shapes with 2, 1 and 0 lines of reflective symmetry.

(Some examples of shapes.)

3 How many lines of reflective symmetry do these shapes have?

a. Square — **4**   c. Regular pentagon — **5**

b. Regular hexagon — **6**   d. Regular octagon — **8**

4 Use all the mirror lines to complete these patterns.

a.   b.

5 Use all the mirror line to reflect this shape.

Name: _____   Date: _____

1 How many lines of reflective symmetry do these shapes have?

a.   b.    c.    d.

| _____ line(s) | _____ line(s) | _____ line(s) | _____ line(s) |

2 Draw three shapes with 2, 1 and 0 lines of reflective symmetry.

3 How many lines of reflective symmetry do these shapes have?

a. Square [   ]   c. Regular pentagon [   ]

b. Regular hexagon [   ]   d. Regular octagon [   ]

4 Use all the mirror lines to complete these patterns.

a.   b.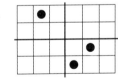

5 Use the mirror line to reflect this shape.

Activity sheet questions

- Recognise properties of rectangles.
  Classify triangles (isosceles, equilateral, scalene), using criteria such as equal sides, equal angles, lines of symmetry.
- Classify solid shapes.
  Make shapes with increasing accuracy.
  Visualise 3D shapes from 2D drawings and identify different nets for an open cube.
- Recognise reflective symmetry in regular polygons: for example, know that a square has four axes of symmetry and an equilateral triangle has three.
  Complete symmetrical patterns with two lines of symmetry at right angles (using squared paper or pegboard).
  Recognise where a shape will be after reflection in a mirror line parallel to one side (sides not all parallel or perpendicular to the mirror line).

Written

1 **Recognise where a shape will be after a translation.**

2–5 ● **Recognise positions and directions:**
  – read and plot co-ordinates in the first quadrant

6 **– recognise perpendicular and parallel lines.**

- Understand and use angle measure in degrees.
  Identify, estimate and order acute and obtuse angles.
  Use a protractor to measure and draw acute and obtuse angles to the nearest 5°.
  Calculate angles in a straight line.

Teacher note

- Children can memorise such phrases as 'in the house and up the stairs', 'x is across, x is a cross' or 'along the corridor and up the stairs' to help them remember the order in which we read the co-ordinates.
- Children will require a ruler for this assessment.

Answers

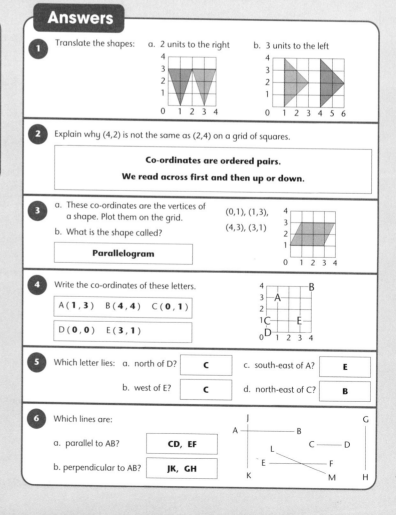

1 Translate the shapes: a. 2 units to the right   b. 3 units to the left

2 Explain why (4,2) is not the same as (2,4) on a grid of squares.

> **Co-ordinates are ordered pairs.**
>
> **We read across first and then up or down.**

3 a. These co-ordinates are the vertices of a shape. Plot them on the grid.   (0,1), (1,3), (4,3), (3,1)
   b. What is the shape called?

   Parallelogram

4 Write the co-ordinates of these letters.

   A (**1** , **3**)   B (**4** , **4**)   C (**0** , **1**)

   D (**0** , **0**)   E (**3** , **1**)

5 Which letter lies: a. north of D? **C**   c. south-east of A? **E**

   b. west of E? **C**   d. north-east of C? **B**

6 Which lines are:

   a. parallel to AB? **CD, EF**

   b. perpendicular to AB? **JK, GH**

Name: _____ Date: _____

Shape and space

1 Translate the shapes: a. 2 units to the right b. 3 units to the left.

2 Explain why (4,2) is not the same as (2,4) on a grid of squares.

3 a. These co-ordinates are the vertices of a shape. Plot them on the grid.

(0,1), (1,3), (4,3), (3,1)

b. What is the shape called?

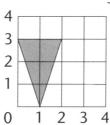

4 Write the co-ordinates of these letters.

A(,) B(,) C(,)

D(,) E(,)

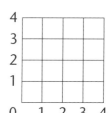

5 Which letter lies: a. north of D? [   ] c. south-east of A? [   ]

b. west of E? [   ] d. north-east of C? [   ]

6 Which lines are:

a. parallel to AB? [   ]

b. perpendicular to AB? [   ]

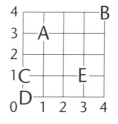

Activity sheet questions

- Recognise properties of rectangles.
  Classify triangles (isosceles, equilateral, scalene),using criteria such as equal sides, equal angles, lines of symmetry.
- Classify solid shapes.
  Make shapes with increasing accuracy.
  Visualise 3D shapes from 2D drawings and identify different nets for an open cube.
- Recognise reflective symmetry in regular polygons: for example, know that a square has four axes of symmetry and an equilateral triangle has three.
  Complete symmetrical patterns with two lines of symmetry at right angles (using squared paper or pegboard).
  Recognise where a shape will be after reflection in a mirror line parallel to one side (sides not all parallel or perpendicular to the mirror line).
  Recognise where a shape will be after a translation.
- Recognise positions and directions:
  - read and plot co-ordinates in the first quadrant
  - recognise perpendicular and parallel lines.

Written

1	● **Understand and use angle measure in degrees.**
2–3	**Identify, estimate and order acute and obtuse angles.**
4–6	**Use a protractor to measure and draw acute and obtuse angles to the nearest 5°.**
7	**Calculate angles in a straight line.**

Teacher note

- Children need to see a varied range of drawings of angles.
  Avoid only referring to those that have lines the same length and a horizontal line (especially in right-angled shapes).
- The children will require a protractor during this assessment.

Answers

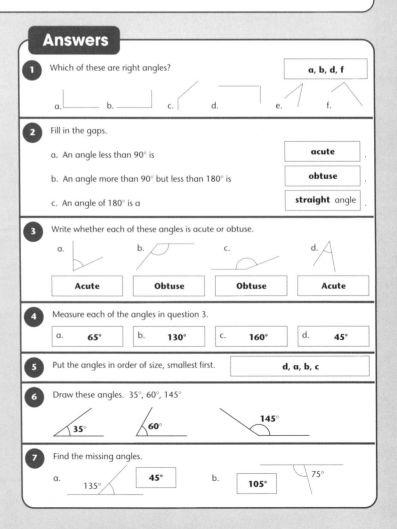

1 Which of these are right angles?
a. b. c. d. e. f.

a, b, d, f

2 Fill in the gaps.

a. An angle less than 90° is

acute

b. An angle more than 90° but less than 180° is

obtuse

c. An angle of 180° is a

straight angle

3 Write whether each of these angles is acute or obtuse.

a. b. c. d.

Acute **Obtuse** **Obtuse** **Acute**

4 Measure each of the angles in question 3.

a. **65°** b. **130°** c. **160°** d. **45°**

5 Put the angles in order of size, smallest first.

d, a, b, c

6 Draw these angles. 35°, 60°, 145°

35° **60°** **145°**

7 Find the missing angles.

a. 135° **45°** b. **105°** 75°

Name: _____   Date: _____

1 Which of these are right angles?

[ ]

a. └─────┘   b. └─────   c.   d. ⌐─────   e.   f.

2 Fill in the gaps.

a. An angle less than 90° is [ ] .

b. An angle more than 90° but less than 180° is [ ] .

c. An angle of 180° is a [angle] .

3 Write whether each of these angles is acute or obtuse.

a.   b.   c.   d.

[ ]   [ ]   [ ]   [ ]

4 Measure each of the angles in question 3.

| a. | b. | c. | d. |

5 Put the angles in order of size, smallest first.   [ ]

6 Draw these angles. 35°, 60°, 145°

7 Find the missing angles.

a.
135°   [ ]

b. [ ]
75°

Record sheet

(Duplicate for class use.)

Number of answers

Names	Assessment No. 1	2	3	4	5	6	7	8	9	10	11	12	13	14	15	16	17	18	19	20	21	22	23	24	25	26	27	28	29	30	31	32	33	34

MATHS WEEKLY ASSESSMENT: *Book 5*

© Folens (copiable page)